G. SCHIRMER'S COLLECTION OF OPERAS.

LOHENGRIN

A ROMANTIC OPERA

In Three Acts

WRITTEN AND COMPOSED BY

RICHARD WAGNER

TRANSLATED INTO ENGLISH BY

NATALIA MACFARREN

G. SCHIRMER — NEW YORK.

Lohengrin.

FIRST PERFORMED AT WEIMAR, GERMANY, AUGUST 28, 1850.

Characters of the Drama.

LOHENGRIN, Knight of the Holy Grail	Tenor.
HENRY I., King of Germany	Bass.
FREDERICK TELRAMUND, a Noble of Brabant . . .	Baritone.
THE ROYAL HERALD	Bass.
GOTTFRIED, Elsa's brother, mute personage.	
FOUR NOBLES OF BRABANT	Tenors and Basses.
ELSA OF BRABANT	Soprano.
ORTRUD, wife of Telramund	Mezzo-soprano.
FOUR PAGES	Soprano and Alto

Chorus of Saxon and Brabantian Nobles, Ladies, Pages, etc.

THE SCENE PASSES IN ANTWERP; PERIOD, THE FIRST HALF OF THE 10th CENTURY.

The Story of Lohengrin.

ACT I.—Henry "the Fowler", King of Germany, has come to Antwerp to summon his lieges against the Hungarians, who threaten the eastern frontier; he finds the chiefs divided and without a leader—Gottfried, the young son of the late Duke, having mysteriously disappeared, and Frederick Telramund, in virtue of his wife's royal descent, claiming the sovereignty of Brabant. Telramund openly accuses Elsa (Gottfried's sister) of having murdered her brother to win the crown for herself; Elsa is summoned to appear and answer the charge; the King decrees that her cause shall be submitted to ordeal of battle between Telramund and any champion Elsa may choose to defend her. She describes a Knight whom she has seen in a vision, and conjures him to fight for her. After repeated appeals, a skiff, drawn by a swan, is seen to approach the shore; in it is Lohengrin Elsa's chosen Knight, who accepts Telramund's challenge. Before they fight, Lohengrin betroths himself to Elsa, first claiming her solemn promise never to question him as to his name or race, nor whence he came to her; Telramund is overcome in the combat, and stripped of lands and honors.

ACT II.—Telramund and Ortrud (his wife) are watching outside the Palace, which resounds with mirth and revelry; they are determined yet to accomplish the ruin of Elsa and Lohengrin, and be reinstated in their former rank. Elsa appears on the balcony, and to her Ortrud makes a piteous appeal, which so effectually moves Elsa to compassion, that she promises to obtain the reprieve of Telramund's sentence. She offers to shelter Ortrud for the night, who, amid false protestations of gratitude, affects concern for the uncertainty of Elsa's future happiness, and contrives to insinuate the first germs of suspicion in Elsa's mind. They enter the abode of Elsa. The retainers and vassals assemble to form the bridal procession. Ortrud appears in the train of Elsa's ladies ; arrived at the steps of the Minster, she cannot restrain her haughty temper, and disputes Elsa's right of precedence ; in the midst of the ensuing commotion the King and Lohengrin enter. Lohengrin reproves his bride for holding converse with the evil-minded woman ; they are proceeding to the church when Telramund interposes and accuses Lohengrin of sorcery, alleging the strange manner of his coming amongst them, and the mystery in which his name and rank are shrouded, in support of the declaration. The faith of the King and his Knights in Lohengrin, however, remains unshaken ; doubts for a moment overwhelm Elsa, but she casts them aside ; the train finally enters the church, and they are united.

Act III.—Elsa and Lohengrin are conducted to the bridal chamber by a train of Knights and Ladies, and for the first time are alone ; doubt and suspicion by this time having taken complete possession of Elsa's mind, she questions her husband with growing vehemence, unmindful of his warnings that her doubts must end their happiness, for, if she insist, to *her* he must reveal his secret. When their altercation is at its height a murderous attempt is made on Lohengrin's life by Telramund and four of his followers. Elsa, quick to perceive their intent, hands Lohengrin his sword, who strikes Telramund dead with a single blow. He then places Elsa in the care of her Ladies, charging them to lead her into the presence of the King. Before the King he meets her once more and reveals himself to be the son of Percival, and a Knight of the Holy Grail ; being known, he is now bound to return to its mysterious guardianship. As he speaks, the swan, drawing the skiff, appears again on the river, and to Elsa's unspeakable grief, he bids her an eternal farewell. Before he steps into the skiff he disenchants the swan, who is no other than Gottfried, transformed by Ortrud's sorcery, and who now takes rightful possession of his Dukedom.

Lohengrin.

When Richard Wagner was collecting the materials out of which he built the wonderfully tragic and powerful "Tannhäuser", he naturally read the famous old medieval poem "Der Wartburgkrieg". This poem, narrating the story of a notable contest of song at the Wartburg Castle, dealt with Wolfram von Eschenbach as if he were a legendary personage. Wagner, knowing that he was a reality, procured his great epic, "Parzival", and reading it with enthusiasm, drew from it much of the material used in the construction of his music-drama "Parsifal" and his more lyric work "Lohengrin". It was while passing the summer of 1845 at Marienbad that Wagner laid out the plan of the most popular lyric opera of our time. He wrote the book in the course of the following winter, and the music the next year.

It must not be supposed that he accepted the insufficient outline of the story as found in Wolfram's poem. Wagner's method of literary composition was to gather all the versions of a national mythological legend, and select the incidents and characters which fitted into his plan, which was always determined by dramatic propriety and ethical purpose. Franz Muncker, in his excellent and compact sketch of Wagner's life and works, tells us that in Paris the poet-composer had become acquainted with the medieval poem of a Bavarian author recounting the history of Lohengrin, son of Parsifal, Keeper of the Holy Grail, and of his journey to Elsa of Brabant. He also read the legend in its old popular form as related in the "Deutsche Sagen" of the Grimm Brothers, and he made use of parts of Conrad von Würzburg's "Schwanritter", of the "Younger Titurel", and of the old Teutonic belief that through magic human beings can be transformed into swans.

In the winter of 1845 the master arranged the situations and invented the principal themes of his work. He began the composition of the music with the narrative of Lohengrin in the last scene of the third act, because, like Senta's ballad in "The Flying Dutchman", that passage contained the musical germs of the whole work. The third act, then, was composed between September 9, 1846, and March 5, 1847, while he was at Grossgraufen, near Pillnitz. The first act was composed between May 12 and June 8, 1847. The second act was written between June 18 and August 2, 1847, and the prelude was completed on August 28 of the same year. The instrumentation occupied the composer during the following winter and spring. The score of the opera remained unpublished for some years, because Meser, who had brought out Wagner's previous works, had lost much money by them, and declined to touch "Lohengrin". The rights of publication where subsequently acquired at a small price by Breitkopf & Härtel.

Managers were equally unwilling to risk the fortunes of a public production of a new work by a much-criticized and generally misunderstood master. Wagner tells us how he took out the score one day, and gazing at it, was filled with sorrow that the notes might never "sound from off the death-pale paper". In despair he wrote to Liszt, his good friend and the musical god of Weimar, begging him to perform the work, and back came the answer that it was already in preparation. Wagner himself did not hear "Lohengrin" till 1859, but it was produced at Weimar, Liszt conducting, on August 28, 1850. The original cast consisted of Fräulein Agthe as Elsa, Fräulein Faisstlinger as Ortrud, Herr Beck as Lohengrin, Milde as Telramund, Höfer as King Henry, "Lohengrin" was first given at Wiesbaden in 1853, Leipsic, Schwerin, Frankfort, Darmstadt, Breslau, and Stettin in 1854; Cologne, Hamburg, Riga, and Prague, 1855; Munich and Vienna, 1858; Berlin and Dresden, 1859; New York in Italian, 1874, in German, 1884; in London, 1875; and in Paris, 1887. It is to-day performed on the continent of Europe more frequently than any other opera.

The action of "Lohengrin" takes place in the tenth century. At the rise of the curtain King Henry is seen seated on his throne in a meadow. He has come to urge the nobles of Brabant to defense against a Hungarian invasion, and also to investigate domestic troubles. Count Telramund accuses Elsa, daughter of the late Duke of Brabant, and Telramund's ward, of murdering her brother. He demands that he, as next heir to the Duke, be made ruler of Brabant and that Elsa be punished. Elsa is summoned, and instead of defending herself, tells of her vision of a knight who is to be her defender and her lord. The dispute between her and Telramund is, according to the custom, submitted to the ordeal of combat. Elsa declares that the knight of her vision will be her champion. After she has prayed, he appears, coming down the river in a boat drawn by a swan. He asks Elsa to be his wife, but exacts from her a promise never to ask who he is or whence he came. She promises. The combat follows. Lohengrin triumphs, but spares Telramund's life.

The second act reveals Telramund and his wife Ortrud sitting in disgrace and sorrow on the steps of the palace at Antwerp. A scene of bitter recrimination between them, fully explained by its text, follows. Ortrud, however, tells Telramund that she will instil doubt into Elsa's mind and lead her to ask Lohengrin the fatal question, when he will at once leave her and return to his home. Elsa appears on her balcony and Ortrud appeals to her. The maiden descends, and Ortrud at once begins her evil labor. The two go into the palace together. Morning dawns, and the Herald of the King proclaims Telramund an outlaw and Lohengrin ruler of Brabant. The bridal procession appears and is about to enter the church when Ortrud interposes, claims precedence over Elsa, and declares that Lohengrin is a sorcerer. The King and Lohengrin appear and end this scene. The procession again advances, to be interrupted again, this time by Telramund, who repeats his wife's accusations. After a further attempt by Telramund to shake the faith of Elsa, the procession enters the cathedral.

The third act begins with the arrival of the bridal couple in their apartments, accompanied by the King and the nobles. The lovers are left alone, and now Elsa's curiosity gets the better of her devotion. Finally, she asks the question, and at that instant Telramund and four companions enter with drawn swords. Elsa hurriedly gives Lohengrin his own sword and he slays Telramund. Elsa now realizes the significance of her error, but Lohengrin summons her women and bids them take her to the King, before whom he will reveal his name and station.

The second scene of this act takes place in the meadow by the river. Telramund's body is borne on, and Elsa and Lohengrin also arrive. Lohengrin announces that he cannot be the leader of the warriors. He now tells his story. He is Lohengrin, the son of Parsifal, Keeper of the Holy Grail, and as one of the Grail Knights he is endowed with power to defend the innocent, but only so long as he preserves the secret of his name and rank. Now that these are told, he must break his own heart as well as Elsa's by a final departure. The swan returns with the boat. Ortrud, in this moment of triumph, cannot refrain from declaring that the swan is no other than Elsa's missing brother changed into a bird by her enchantments. Lohengrin prays, the swan is retransformed into Elsa's brother, and a dove draws away the boat containing the Knight of the Grail.

It would not be at all difficult to write a long essay on the music of " Lohengrin ", but this is not the place for it. The work belongs to what is known as Wagner's transition-period. It stands between the two earlier works, in which old operatic forms and traditions are to a considerable extent preserved, and the later creations of the master, in which his own theories are fully developed. In " Lohengrin " we first meet with Wagner's " continuous melody ". There are no separate numbers as there were in the old operas, and as there are even in "Tannhäuser", but the music flows spontaneously in faithful accompaniment to the suggestions of the text from the beginning of each act to the end.

A natural result of this plan is the firm and convincing coherency of the music. The style is absolutely unique, and its individuality is preserved from beginning to end. Only in the beginning of the second act is there a complete departure from the essentially sweet and fluent character of the melody ; but the duet between Ortrud and Telramund is, perhaps, the most satisfactory exposition of Wagner's genius in the whole work. Certainly nowhere else in "Lohengrin" do poetry, scenic painting, music, and action unite so perfectly in the production of that dramatic totality which Wagner called the art-work of the future. I recommend to those who sincerely desire to understand Wagner's theory of operatic art a careful study of this scene, not alone in the score, but in the theatre, where only it is to be observed in its entirety.

Leading-motives are used in this opera, but only incidentally, as they were in "Tannhäuser". The system had not reached its perfection in the master's mind, and the "typical phrase" had not yet become the entire material of his music. Nevertheless, the most important personages, objects, and emotions have their musical embodiments in the score of "Lohengrin". If anything were to be gained by making a catalogue of them, I should insert one here ; but there is altogether too much cataloguing of leading-motives. There is nothing in the music of any Wagner drama which is not fully explained by the text, and it is only necessary to bear in mind the fact that Wagner aimed at an organic union between poetry and music, and not a mere production of ear-tickling sounds. Furthermore, general consent seems to have excepted "Lohengrin" from the necessity of explanation. No one writes handbooks to it, and no one lectures about it. This is not because it is a more satisfactory work of art than any other work of Wagner, but because, while its musical form is radically different from that of the distinctively Italian opera, its musical style is immediately appreciable by the least-educated ear. An examination of the score will show that it teems with beautiful and original ideas, and that it is a remarkable embodiment of musical skill and learning. But the results are : apparent spontaneity, a wealth of melodic beauty, and a gorgeousness of vocal and instrumental color, which inspire the imagination and move the heart.

"Lohengrin" has for years been the most popular opera in America when presented with a satisfactory company of singers. It has had some admirable casts. One of the best that ever sang it in Italian was that of the season of 1883–1884 at the Metropolitan Opera House, when Christine Nilsson was the Elsa, Emma Fursch-Madi the Ortrud, Italo Campanini the Lohengrin, Guiseppe Kaschmann the Telramund, and Francesco Novara the King. But undoubtedly the best cast ever assembled in this country, and one of the best in the history of the work, was that which performed "Lohengrin" in German at the Metropolitan in the season of 1895–1896. Mme. Lillian Nordica was the Elsa, Mme. Marie Brema the Ortrud, M. Jean de Reszké the Lohengrin, M. Kaschmann the Telramund, and M. Edouard de Reszké the King.

W. J. Henderson.

Index.

Lohengrin.

Jan 25 - 1947

Helen Traubel Elsa
Lauritz Melchior —
Margaret Harshaw — Ortrud
Hawkins Telramund
Fritz Busch — Director
Thompson Hugh Herald
Engar King Henry new bass

Jany 7 - 1950

26 Clear Traubel Helen
Melchior L.
Varnay Astrid
Janssen Herald
Ernster
Stiedry
conductor

84° Clr July 30 - 1950
Recordings part of
Kurt Baum Lohengrin
Helen Traubel
NY Philharmonic Orch
W.B.B.M.

Lohengrin.

PRELUDE.

RICHARD WAGNER.

3 Flutes, 2 Oboes, 1 Corno inglese, 2 Clarinets in A, 1 Bass Clarinet, 3 Bassoons, Horns in E & D, 3 Trumpets in D, 3 Trombones, Tuba, Kettle-Drums in A & E, Cymbals, 4 Solo Violins, & Strings.

Printed in the U. S. A.

p
8
Ped.
dim.
sempre piano.
Tnr., 'Cello, Hns., Bssn. & D. Bass.

Tpts. & Tromb.
cresc.
ff
Tutti.
ff
diminuendo.
Str.
p molto tran-
quillo.
più p
più p
Tpts.
Tromb.
pp
Fl.
Vl.
Vl. & Fl.
Vl. only.
4 Solo Vls.

Act I.

First Scene.

2 Flutes, 2 Oboes, 2 Clarinets in B♭, 3 Bassoons, Horns in E & D, 3 Trumpets in F, 3 Trombones, Tuba, Kettle-Drums in C, & Strings.

(Here the curtain rises.— A meadow on the banks of the Scheldt near Antwerp. King Henry under the Oak of Justice, surrounded by the Counts and Nobles of the Saxon arrière-ban.)

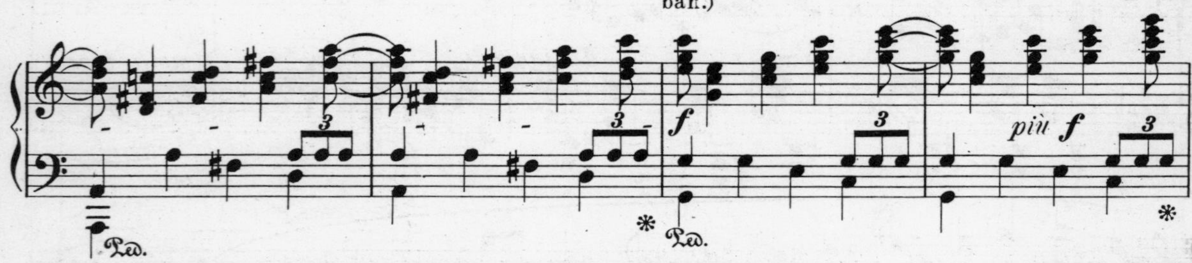

(Opposite to them the Counts and Nobles of Brabant, headed by Frederick of Telramund, with Ortrud by his side. The Herald advances from the party of the King to the centre of the stage; on a sign from him, four royal Trumpeters blow a summons.)

bant! Hein - rich, der Deut-schen Kö - nig, kam zur
bant! Hen - ry, our Ger-man Sov' - reign, calls ye

p Hns. fp Tpts. fp

Ped. *

Andante.

Statt, mit euch zu din-gen nach des Rei - ches Recht. Gebt ihr nun
forth, this day to mus-ter for the realm's de - fence. Will ye as

p Str. f

Ped. *

Fried' und Fol - ge dem Ge - bot?
faith - ful vas - sals serve your King?

Tempo I. TENORS. f

The Brabantians. Chorus.

Wir ge - ben
We will as

BASSES. f

Wir ge - ben
We will as

Tempo I.

p p cresc.

Fried' und Fol - ge dem Ge - bot! Will-kom - men, will-
faith - ful vas - sals serve our King! Be wel - come, be

ff

Fried' und Fol - ge dem Ge - bot! Will-kom - men, will-
faith - ful vas - sals serve our King! Be wel - come, be

ff

f p molto cresc.

Ped. * Ped. *

(clashing their arms.)
kom- -men, Kö-nig, in Bra-bant!
wel- -come, Hen-ry, to Bra-bant!
kom- -men, Kö-nig, in Bra-bant!
wel- -come, Hen-ry, to Bra-bant!
4 Tpts. on the stage.
ff
dim.
(The King rises.) King Henry.
Gott grüss' euch, lie-be
Heav'n shield ye, loy-al
Orch.
f
ff
Wind.
(Freely declaimed.)
(emphatically.)
Män-ner von Bra-bant! Nicht müssig that zu euch ich die-se Fahrt; der Noth des
lieg-es of Bra-bant! Not i-dly have I journey'd to your shores; I come to
Str.
ff
p
Rei-ches seid von mir ge-mahnt!
warn, that dan-ger is at hand!
(All listen with grave attention.)
Soll
Ye
Maestoso.
ff
ffp

ich euch erst der Drangsal Kun-de sa-gen, die deut-sches Land so
know full well the tide of death and ru-in that oft hath from the
oft aus O-sten traf? In fern-ster Mark hiesst Weib und Kind ihr
east swept o'er the land? Up-on our fron-tiers pray the wives and
be-ten: „Herr Gott, be-wahr' uns vor der Un-garn Wuth!“ Doch
chil-dren: "Lord, from th' Hung-a-rian hordes pro-tect our hearths!" For
Wind.
Str.
mir, des Reiches Haupt, musst' es ge-zie-men, solch wil-der Schmach ein En-de zu er-
me, the nation's guard-ian, it was fit-ting to make an end of mis-rule and op-
sin-nen; als Kam-pfes Preis ge-wann ich Frie-den auf neun
pression. As con-quer-or, at last I gain'd a nine years'
Allegro.

in time.

Jahr, ihn nützt' ich zu des Rei - ches Wehr; be - schirm - te
truce, that time I used to arm the land; with walls and

Tpts. *f* Ped. *

Städt' und Bur - gen liess ich bau'n, den Heer - bann üb - te ich zum
tow'rs I for - ti - fied the towns, and now a - gainst the foe I

mf *Wind.* *p* *fp*

Wi - derstand. Zu End' ist nun die Frist, der Zins ver-
sum - mon you. The term is just o'er-past, the foe pre-

Tpts. *f* *p cresc.* *f* *f*

sagt, mit wil - dem Drohen rüs - tet sich der Feind.
pares, the wont - ed tribute I re - fuse to pay.

ff *ffp* *p cresc.*

Allegro. *(with much warmth.)*

Nun ist es Zeit, des Rei - ches Ehr' zu
Now is the time to guard our na - tion's

f

wah - ren; ob Ost, ob West? Das gel-te Al-len
hon - or; from East, and West, all men of Ger-man
gleich! Was deutsches Land heisst, stel - le Kam-pfes-
blood, a-rise u-nit-ed, Knights, your thralls as-
Tpts. & Trombs.
più f
mf
schaa-ren, dann schmäht wohl Nie - mand mehr das deut-sche
sem-ble, No man shall dare de-ride my sov-'reign
p
ff
Reich!
rule.
The Saxons (clashing their arms.)
Chorus.
Wohl auf für deut - schen Rei - ches
'Tis well, we'll guard our Ger - man
f
Mit Gott für Rei - ches
We'll guard our Ger - man
ff
p
molto cresc.

(The King has resumed his seat.)
Ehr'! land!
Ehr'! land!
ff
dim.
The King (slower, freely declaimed.)
Komm' ich zu euch nun, Männer von Brabant, zur Hee-res-folg' nach Mainz euch zu ent-
Thus have I sought ye, Freemen of Brabant, to summon you to Mentz, nobles and
Str.
p
bie-ten, wie muss mit Schmerz und Kla-gen ich er-seh'n, dass oh-ne
vas-sals; here to my grief I meet with naught but strife, All in dis-
Für-sten ihr in Zwie-tracht lebt! Ver-wir-rung, wil-de
u-nion, from your chiefs e-strang'd! Con-fu-sion, civ-il
Feh-de wird mir kund; drum ruf' ich dich, Friedrich von Tel-ra-mund! Ich
war-fare meet me here. On thee I call, Fred'rick of Tel-ra-mund! I
f
p

ken-ne dich als al-ler Tu-gend Preis, jetzt re-de, dass der Drangsal Grund ich
know thee for a knight as brave, as true; I charge thee, let me know this trouble's
Frederick (with solemnity.)
weiss.
cause.
Maestoso.
Wind.
Str.
Dank, König, dir, dass du zu rich-ten kamst!
Thanks, gracious King, that thou to judge art come!
Die Wahr-heit künd' ich, Un-treu' ist mir fremd!
The truth I'll tell thee, falsehood I dis-dain.
Zum Ster-ben kam der Her-zog von Bra-bant, und mei-nem
When death was clos-ing round our val-iant Duke, 'twas me he
Schutz empfahl er sei-ne Kin-der, El-sa, die Jungfrau, und Gottfried, den
chose as guard-ian of his chil-dren, El-sa, the maid-en, and Gottfried her

Knaben; mit Treu - e pflag ich sei - ner gro - ssen Ju - gend, sein
brother; whose dawn - ing years with ten - der care I guarded, whose
p
Ped.
Le - ben war das Klein - od mei - ner Eh - re. Er - miss nun,
wel - fare I have treasur'd as my hon - or. My sov'reign,
With spirit.
ff
ffp
Kö - nig, meinen grimmen Schmerz, als mei - ner Eh - re Kleinod mir ge -
mark now, if I am ag - griev'd, when of my hon - or's treasure I am
fp
f
raubt! Lust-wandelnd führ - te El - sa den Knaben einst zum
robb'd! One day when El - sa had with her brother wan - der'd
Fast.
ff
p Str.
Wald, doch oh - ne ihn kehr - te sie zu - rück; mit fal - scher Sor - ge frug sie nach dem
forth, with - out the boy trembling she re - turn'd; with feign'd la - ment - ing question'd of his
f
p

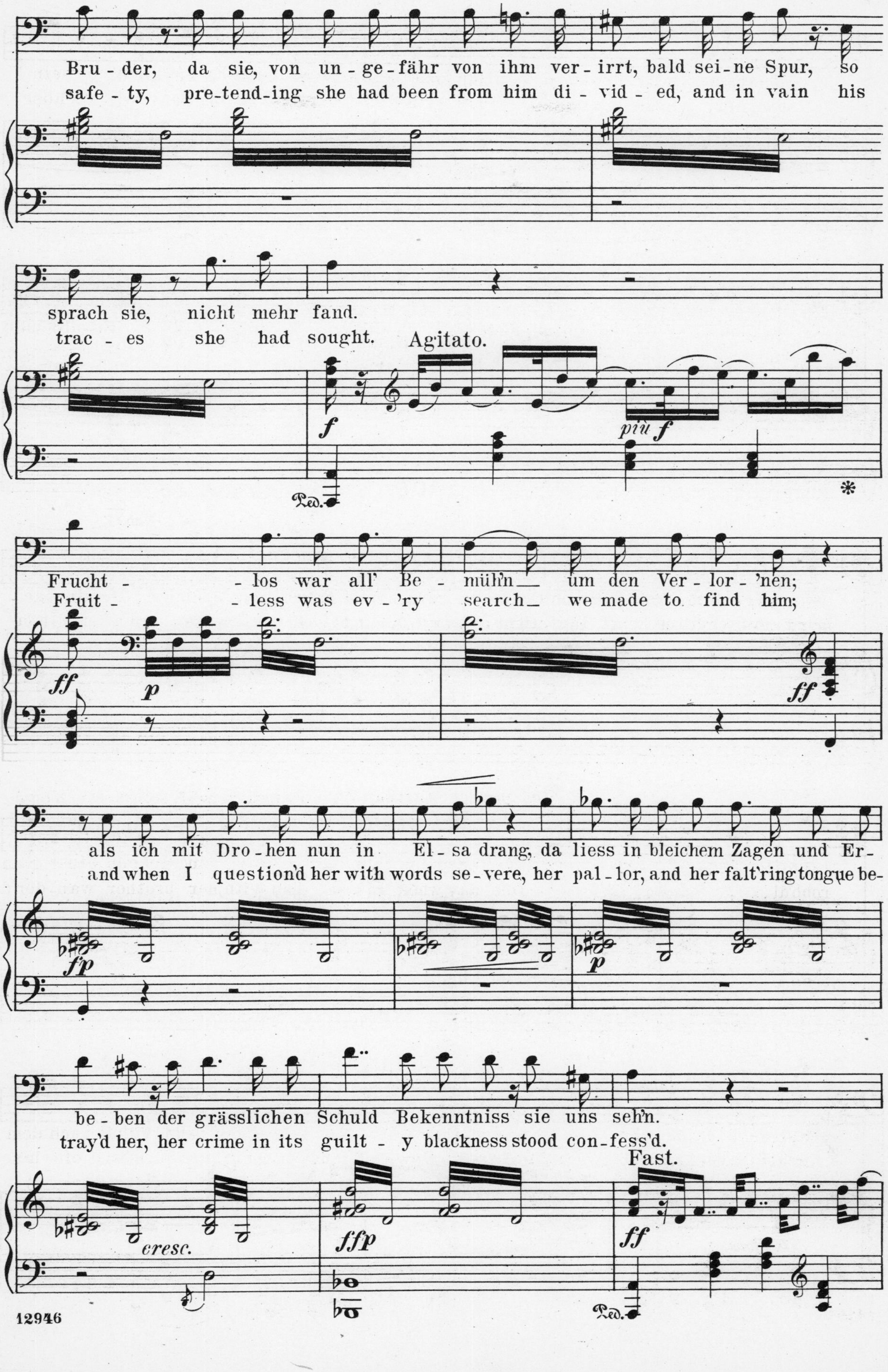
Bru - der, da sie, von un - ge - fähr von ihm ver - irrt, bald sei - ne Spur, so
safe - ty, pre - tend - ing she had been from him di - vid - ed, and in vain his
sprach sie, nicht mehr fand.
trac - es she had sought.
Agitato.
f
più f
Frucht - los war all' Be - müh'n um den Ver - lor - 'nen;
Fruit - less was ev - 'ry search we made to find him;
ff
p
ff
als ich mit Dro - hen nun in El - sa drang, da liess in bleichem Zagen und Er -
and when I question'd her with words se - vere, her pal - lor, and her falt'ring tongue be -
fp
p
be - ben der grässlichen Schuld Bekenntniss sie uns seh'n.
tray'd her, her crime in its guilt - y blackness stood con - fess'd.
Fast.
cresc.
ffp
ff

(Very animated.)
Es fasste mich En-set-zen vor der
A horror fell up-on me of the
fp
Magd: dem Recht auf ih-re Hand, vom Va-ter mir ver-
maid, the claim up-on her hand her fa-ther had con-
fp
lieh'n, ent-sagt' ich wil-lig da und gern, und nahm ein Weib, das
ferr'd, with will-ing heart I straight re-sign'd, and chose a wife full
p
mf
dim.
(he presents Ortrud, who inclines herself before the King.)
mei-nem Sinn ge-fiel: Or-trud, Radbod's, des Frie-sen-für-sten
pleas-ant to my sense, Or-trud, daughter of Radbod, true in
p
f Trom.
Rather slowly. (he advances a few paces with measured step.)
Spross. Nun führ' ich
death. I here ar-
p
D. Bass.
f ff

Kla - ge wi - der El - sa von Bra - bant: des
raign her, Princess El - sa of Bra - bant, of
ff Hns.
fp Trombs.
ff Str.
Bru - der - mor - des zeih' ich sie. Diess
frat - ri - cide be she charg'd. I
ff Hns.
fp Trombs.
ff Str.
Land doch sprech' ich für mich an mit Recht, da ich der
claim do - min - ion o'er this land by right, My near - est
ff
Nächste von des Her - zogs Blut, mein Weib da - zu aus dem Ge -
kinsman was the val - iant Duke, my wife de - scend - ant of the
f
p
f
schlecht, das einst auch die - sen Landen sei - ne Für - sten gab.
race that gave this land their rul - ers thro' long a - ges past.
f
Trombs.
D. Bass.
ff

Du hörst die Kla - ge, Kö - nig! Richte
Oh King, give judgment, all now thou hast
ff Wind.
dim.
p Str.
Not dragging.
recht!
heard.
p TENOR I.
Mit
I
p TENOR II.
Chorus.
All the Men (awe-struck.)
p
BASS I.
Ha, schwe - rer Schuld zeiht Tel - ra - mund! Mit
Ha, Tel - ra - mund, what hast thou said? I
BASS II.
Not dragging.
pp
Graun werd' ich der Kla - ge
mark thee with dis may and
cresc.
Graun werd' ich der Kla - ge
mark thee with dis may and
poco cresc.
più p

The King.
Welch' fürch-ter-li-che Kla - ge sprichst du aus!
A dread-ful ac-cu - sa - tion thou hast brought!
kund!
dread!
kund!
dread!
kund!
dread!
Tnr.
p
Bssn.
Frederick. (becoming more vehement.)
Wie wä - re mög-lich sol-che gro - sse Schuld? O Herr,
A crime so dead-ly how can I be - lieve? Oh King,
traum-se-lig ist die eit - le Magd, die mei-ne Hand voll
list - less and dream-y is the maid, she who with scorn re -
fp

(gradual-
Hochmuth von sich stiess. Ge-hei-mer Buhl-schaft klag' ich drum sie an: sie
fus'd my proffer'd hand. Some se-cret love her sens-es hath be-guil'd; she
fp
fp
fp
ly becoming more and more excited.)
wähn-te wohl, wenn sie des Bru-ders le-dig, dann könn-te sie als
deem'd, per-chance, be-cause the boy had per-ish'd, she'd reign se-cure as
f Tnr.
p
Her-rin von Bra-bant mit Recht dem Lehnsmann ih-re Hand ver-
sov'reign of Bra-bant, for that, her vas-sal she dis-dain'd as
f
p
(The King, with a grave gesture, reproves Frederick's vehemence.)
weh-ren, und of-fen des ge-hei-men Buh-len pfle-gen.
con-sort, that o-pen-ly she might her lov-er cher-ish.
Molto Allegro.
cresc.
f
The King.
(with great solemnity.)
Ruft die Be-klag-te her! Be-gin-nen
Sum-mon the maid ac-cus'd! For judg-ment
ff
ff
ff
Ped.
*

Slower.
soll nun das Ge - richt! Gott lass mich wei - se sein!
let all be pre - par'd! Heav'n, let me deem a - right!
ritard. time rather slower. 4 Tpts. on the stage.
Trombs. dim.
Str.
(The Herald steps into the centre with solemnity.)
Herald.
Soll hier nach Recht und Macht Ge - richt ge - hal - ten sein?
Dost thou de - cree, O King, to hold a judg - ment here?
Tnr. Hns. & Bssn.
The King.
Nicht eh'r soll ber - gen mich der Schild, bis ich ge - rich - tet streng und mild!
I will not rest be - neath my shield, un - til the truth hath been re - veal'd!
slowly.
Trombs. dim.
(All the men bare their swords; the Saxons strike theirs before them into the earth, the Brabantians lay theirs flat on the ground.)
Chorus.
All the Men.
Nicht eh'r zur Schei - de kehr' das
No sword to scab - bard shall re -
molto cresc.

Herald.
Wo ihr des
Where'er the
Schwert, bis ihm durch Ur-theil Recht ge-währt!
turn, until thy will, O King, we learn!
Schwert, bis ihm sein Recht ge-währt!
turn, un-til thy will we learn!
Kö-nigs Schild ge-wahrt, dort Recht durch Ur-theil nun er-
roy-al shield ye see, Know that the king doth there de-
Wind.
fahrt! Drum ruf' ich kla-gend laut und
cree! Re-sound my cry both far and
Tps. & Trombs.
hell: El-sa, er-schei-ne hier zur Stell'!
near: El-sa, thou roy-al maid, ap-pear!
Wind.
Str. pizz.

Scene II.

Elsa enters; she remains awhile at back, then very slowly and timidly advances to the front (centre.) The ladies of her train remain during the first part of the scene in the extreme background, on the outer edge of the judgment-circle.

3 Flutes, 2 Oboes, 1 Corno Inglese, 2 Cls. in B♭, Bass Cl., 3 Bassoons, Horns in F and E flat, 3 Trumpets in E flat, 3 Trombones, Tuba, Kettle-Drums, Strings and Harp.

pp
scheint sie so licht und rein!
an - gel of light her hue!
pp
Wood.
pp
Vl. pizz.
p
Der sie so schwer zu zei-hen wag-te, wie
He who with base sus-pí - cion loads her, Must
p
p
p
The King.
Bist du es, El-sa von Bra-
Art El-sa, lady of Bra-
pp
si - cher muss der Schuld er sein!
prove his dark sur - mise is true!
pp
si - cher muss er sein!
He must prove it true!
Str.
più p
pp
Ped.

(Elsa bows her head in assent.)
bant? Erkennst du mich als deinen
bant? Wilt thou be deem'd by me, thy
Wood.
p
fp
Str.
(Elsa turns her head towards the King, gazes into his eyes, and then makes an affirmative gesture of her complete trust.)
Richter an? So frage ich
sov'reign lord? Then further I
pp
Wood.
weiter; ist die Klage dir bekannt, die schwer hier wider dich erask thee, if the charge to thee is known, that darkly is alleg'd a-
p Str.
(Elsa looks at Frederick and Ortrud, shudders, and sadly inclines her head in assent.)
hoben? Was entgegnest du der Klage?
gainst thee? Canst thou meet the accusation?
f Wood.
più p
ritard.
Str.
(Elsa, by a gesture: "I can say nothing.") with animation.
(Elsa, sadly gazing before her.)
So bekennst du deine Schuld?
Then thy guilt thou dost confess?
Wood.
Str.
pp
fp
f
p

Elsa. (dreamily, to herself.)
Mein ar-mer Bru-der!
Oh my poor broth-er!
All the Men. (whispering.)
pp
Wie wun-der-bar! Welch
'Tis wond-rous strange! Her
pp
Tnr. & 'Cello.
The King. (greatly moved.)
Sag', El-sa! was hast du mir zu ver-
Speak, El-sa! in thy King thou mayst con-
selt-sa-mes Ge-bah-ren!
words I can-not fath-om!
p
>p
Elsa. (gazing tranquilly before her.)
(expectant silence.)
Andante.
trau'n?
fide!
Ein-sam in trü-ben
Oft when the hours were
p Ob.
pizz.
p
Wood.

Tagen hab' ich zu Gott gefleht, des Herzens tiefstes
lonely, I unto Heav'n have pray'd, one boon I ask'd for
Klagen ergoss' ich im Gebet: da drang aus meinem
only, to send the orphans aid; I pray'd in tears and
pp Str.
accel.
Stöhnen ein Laut so klagevoll, der zu gewalt'gem
sorrow, with heavy heart and sore, hoping a brighter
cresc. ed accel.
f
ff
ritard.
Tönen weit in die Lüfte schwoll: ich
morrow yet was for us in store. A-
dim.
hört' ihn fern hin hallen, bis kaum mein Ohr er traf; mein Aug' ist zu gefallen, ich
far my words were wafted, I dreamt not help was nigh, but One on high vouchsaf'd it, while
p Wood.
più p
pp
Str. c. Sord.

Slowly.
sank in sü-ssen Schlaf.
I in sleep did lie.
2nd Chor. 1st Chorus.
TENORS. pp
Träumt sie? Ist sie entrückt?
Wondrous! Or doth she dream?
All the Men.
BASS II. pp
BASS I. pp
Wie son-der-bar!
'Tis passing strange!
Slowly.
Fl.
pp
The King. (as though he would rouse Elsa from a dream.)
El-sa, ver-theid-'ge dich vor dem Ge-richt!
El-sa, de-fend thy-self be-fore thy judge!
poco cresc.
dim.
Hp.
pp
(Elsa's expression changes from dreamy blissfulness to rapturous exaltation.)
Vl. c. Sord.
p
Elsa.
In lich-ter Waf-fen Schei-ne ein
I saw, in splen-dor shin-ing, a
più p
pp
animating the time a little
Rit-ter nah-te da, so
Knight of glo-rious mien, on
p Fl. Ob. Cl. Hp. & Tpts.

tu-gend-li - cher Rei - ne ich kei - nen noch er -
me his eyes in-clin - ing with tran - quil gaze se -
Ped.
sah: ein gol-den Horn zur Hüften, ge-leh - net auf sein
rene, a horn of gold beside him, he leant up-on his
sempre p
Schwert, so trat er aus den Lüf-ten zu
sword, thus when I erst e-spied him 'mid
mir, der Re - cke werth; mit
clouds of light he soar'd; his
Ped.
Ped.
züch - ti-gem Ge-bah - ren gab
words so low and ten - der brought
p

Ten'r, 'Cello, Hp.

(raising her voice.)
Trö - stung er mir ein: des Rit - ters will ich
life re - new'd to me. My guard - ian, my de -
(rapturously)
wah - ren, er soll mein Strei - ter sein! Er
fend - er, thou shalt my cham - pion be! Thou
cresc.
Ped.
rit.
soll mein Strei-ter sein!
shalt my champion be!
All the Men. (much moved.)
pp
Be - wah - re
Oh Heav'n! in
Wind & Hp.
uns des Him - mels Huld, dass
mer - cy be thou near, this

klar wir se - hen, wer hier
day make truth from er - ror
The King.
(more animatedly.)
Fried-rich, du eh-ren-wer-ther Mann, be-den - ke wohl, wen klagst du
Frederick, bethink thee while there's time, could she en - act so foul a
Schuld!
clear!
accel.
Str.
pp
Frederick.
an? Mich ir - ret nicht ihr träu - me - ri - scher
crime? Her dream - y mood my mind hath ne'er de -
Più vivo.
gradually animating the time.
(with growing excitement.)
Muth; ihr hört, sie schwärmt von ei - nem Buh - len! Wes' ich sie
ceiv'd, ye hear, she raves a - bout a lov - er! I speak the

zeih', des' hab' ich si - chern Grund: glaub - wür - dig ward ihr Frevel mir be -
truth, of that I'm well as - sur'd: one do I know who can the deed at -
p Hns.
p
K. Dr.
Ped.
zeugt. Doch eu - rem Zwei - fel durch ein Zeug - niss weh - ren, das
test. But if ye doubt my word as knight or no - ble, no
Tromb.
fp
Str.
fp
stünde wahr - lich ü - bel mei - nem Stoltz! Hier
further proof or wit - ness will I deign! For
fp
f
steh' ich, hier mein Schwert! Wer wagt von euch zu streiten
bat - tle here I stand! Who dares at - taint my hon - or,
ff

Fast.
wi-der meiner Eh- re Preis?
let that man stand forth and fight!
Kei - ner von uns! Wir streiten nur für
I am thy friend! I will not fight with
The Brabantians. (much excited.)
Keiner von uns! Wir streiten nur für
I am thy friend! I will not fight with
Fast.
Und, Kö - nig, du! Gedenkst du meiner Dienste, wie ich im
And thou, my King! re-call to thy re-mem-brance the day I
dich!
thee!
dich!
thee!
ff
dim.
p
f
The King. (with animation.)
Kampf den wil-den Dä-nen schlug? Wie schlimm! liess' ich von dir dar-an mich
sav'd thee from the murd'rous Dane! 'Twere ill if there were need of that to
Str.
fp
f Hns.
fp

mah - nen! Gern geb' ich dir der höch - sten Tu - gend
mind me! Thou'rt brave and true, all hon - or's meed be
p
fp Hns.
Preis; in kei - ner an - dern Huth, als in der dei - nen, möcht' ich die Lan - de
thine, as guardian of this land I'd fain ap - point thee, thou of my chiefs the
Str.
Ped.
(with solemn determination.)
Andante.
wis - sen. Gott al - lein soll
no - blest. Heav'n a - lone shall
f
ff
Wind.
jetzt in die - ser Sa - che noch ent - schei - den!
now for life or death de - cide be - tween you!
ff
All the Men.
Zum Got - tes - ge -
A judg - ment of
ff
Tromb. & Tpts.
p
p
pp
D. Bass.

richt! Zum Got - tes - ge - richt! Wohl -
God! A judg - ment of God! 'Tis

Tur. K. Dr. *cresc.*

(The King draws his sword and strikes it before him into the earth.)

The King.

Dich frag' ich,
An - swer me,

an!
well!

Tromb. & Tb.

Str.

Fried - rich, Graf von Tel - ra - mund! Willst du durch Kampf auf
no - ble Count of Tel - ra - mund! Wilt thou do bat - tle

Trombs.

Le - ben und auf Tod im Got - tes - ge - richt ver -
here for life or death, Shall Heav - en's or - deal de -

dim.

Kr. D.

Frederick.
tre-ten dei-ne Kla-ge? Ja!
cide if thou spok'st tru-ly? Yea!
Tromb.
Str.
K-Dr.
Tromb. & Tb.
The King.
Und dich nun frag' ich, El-sa von Bra-bant!
And now I ask thee, El-sa of Bra-bant:
Str.
Willst du, dass hier auf Le-ben und auf Tod im Got-tes-ge-richt ein
Wilt thou com-mit thy cause for life or death, as Heav-en's or-deal pro-
Trombs.
dim.
K-Dr.
Elsa. (without raising her eyes.)
Ja!
Yea!
Käm-pe für dich strei-te? Wen wäh-lest du zum
nounc-eth by thy cham-pion? Choose one who shall de-
Trombs.
Wood.
Str.
Frederick. (hastily.)
Ver-nehmet jetzt den Na-men ih-res Buh-len!
Now ye shall know the name of her ac-com-plice.
The Brabantians.
Mer-ket auf!
Let us hear!
Strei-ter?
fend thee!
accel.

Più andante. (Elsa has not lost her ecstatic expression; all look towards her with eager expectancy.)
Wood & Hp.
p
Elsa. (firmly.)
Des_ Rit - ters will ich_
My_ guard - ian, my de -
p Str.c.Sord.
wah - ren, er soll mein Strei - ter sein!_
fend - er, He shall my cham - pion be!_
f
dim.
Wood.
(without looking round.)
Hört, was dem Gott - gesand-ten ich bie - te für Ge-
This is the prize I of - fer to him whom Heav'n shall
währ:_ in mei - nes Va - ters Lan - den, die
send:_ the lands and crown I prof - fer, my

Kro - ne tra-ge er; mich glück-lich soll ich
sire to me did lend; as lord I will de -
più p
Str.
Ped.
prei - sen, nimmt er mein Gut da - hin, will
clare him, and glo - ry in his fame, if
Ped.
Ped.
Ped.
Slowly.
er Ge-mahl mich hei - ssen, geb' ich ihm, was ich
in his heart he'll wear me, I'll give him all I
Wind.
pp
f
p
f
p
Ped.
bin!
am!
All the Men. (aside.)
p
pp
Ein schö - ner Preis, stünd' er in Got - tes
A no - ble prize, who will the vic - tor
'Cello.
p
dolce
più p
pp

(to one another.)
Hand! Wer um- ihn stritt',
be? Who will con- tend?
(to one another.)
wohl setzt' er
What will be
Wer um ihn stritt',
Who will con - tend?
The King.
Im Mit - tag hoch steht schon die Son - ne:
The sun stands high, noon will not tar - ry.
schwe - res Pfand.
Heav'n's de - cree?
K.-Dr.
Tromb.
Poco Allegro.
so ist es Zeit, dass nun der Ruf er - geh'!
Call forth the war - rior knight with trum - pet's call.
D. Bass.
(The Herald advances with the four Trumpeters, whom he places towards the four points of the compass at the outer edge of the judgment-circle, where they blow the summons.)
cresc.
4 Tpts. (on the stage.)
Trombs.

Herald.
Wer hier im Got-tes-kampf zu strei-ten kam für El-sa von Bra-bant,
Who will do bat-tle here on life or death for El-sa of Bra-bant,
(Elsa, who till now has preserved perfect tranquillity, shows signs of anxious expectation.)
der tre-te vor! Der tre-te vor!
let him ap-pear! Let him ap-pear!
f Tromb.
p Tur. & Cello pizz.
Frederick. (pointing at Elsa.)
Gewahrt,
Ye see,
All the Men.
pp
Ohn' Ant-wort ist der Ruf ver-hallt!
No cham-pion to the call comes forth!
pp
pp
gewahrt, ob ich sie fälschlich schalt: auf mei-ner
ye see, what now her cause is worth, Both right and
p
Um ih-re Sa-che
Ah, hap-less maid-en,
p
B. Cl.
dim.

Elsa (drawing nearer to the King.)
Sei - te bleibt das Recht! Mein lie - ber Kö - nig, lass dich
power are just - ly mine! My gracious sov'reign, let me
steht es schlecht!
hope re - sign.
Ob.
Wind.
(ingenuously.)
bit - ten, noch ei - nen Ruf an mei - nen Rit - ter! Wohl weilt er
pray thee yet once a - gain my knight to summon, he dwells a -
The King (to the Herald.)
fern und hört' ihn nicht. Noch ein - mal ru - fe zum Ge -
far, and hear - eth not. Once more then let the call go
accel.
Str.
cresc.
più f
(On a sign from the Herald, the Trumpeters again blow towards the four points of the compass.)
richt!
forth.

Herald.
Wer hier im Got-tes-kampf zu strei-ten kam für El-sa von Bra-bant, der tre-te vor! Der tre-te vor!
Who will do bat-tle here on life or death, for El-sa of Bra-bant, let him ap-pear! Let him ap-pear!
4 Tpts. (on the stage.)
Tromb. in Orch.
1 Tpt.
1 Hn.
più p
K.-Dr.
All the Men.
In dü-st'rem Schwei-gen rich-tet Gott!
The Heav'ns are si-lent, she is doom'd!
Trombs.
Molto agitato.
Cl.
dim.
Str.

(Elsa sinks in fervent prayer on her knees; her ladies, concerned for her, come nearer to the front.) **Elsa.**

Du trugest zu ihm
When in my grief I

Cor. ingl. *Vl.* *p*

mei - ne Kla - ge, zu mir trat er auf dein Ge-
bent be - fore Thee, Thou sent - est him who hath my

bot; o Herr, nun mei - nem Rit - ter
vow; oh Lord, hear me a - gain im-

Chorus of the Ladies. (falling on their knees.)

SOPRANOS. *ff* *dim.* *p*

Herr! Sen - de Hül -
Lord! Let Thy help

ALTOS. *ff* *dim.* *p*

Ob. *f* *p*

sa - ge, dass er mir helf' in mei - ner
plore Thee, in my dis - tress, oh send him

f *p*

- fe ihr! Herr Gott!
be nigh! Hear us!

f *p*

f *p*

(with growing exaltation.)
Noth! Lass mich ihn sehn, wie ich ihn
now! Stain - less and white, ra - diant - ly
pp
Hö - re uns!
Gra - cious Lord!
pp
pp
cresc.
sah, wie ich ihn sah, sei er mir
dight, let me be - hold that form of
ff
dim.
(her face beam-
ff
dim.
Wind.
Allegro.
ing with joy.)
p
nah'!
light!
(The First Chorus consists of those standing nearest to the water's edge; they first perceive the coming of Lohengrin, who is seen in the distance approaching in a skiff drawn by a swan.)
TENOR I.
Seht!
Look!
TENOR II.
Seht!
Look!
1st Chorus.
BASS I.
BASS II.
Allegro.
Vls. trem.
pp
3 Tpts.
8

Welch' ein selt - sam Wunder!
This is sure a marvel!
Wie? ein Schwan?
See! a swan!
Welch' ein selt - sam Wunder!
This is sure a marvel!
Wie? ein Schwan?
See! a swan!
Seht! welch' Wunder!
Look! a marvel!
Ein Schwan?
A swan!
sempre p e dolce
Ein Schwan zieht ei - nen Na - chen dort her - an!
A fair swan lead - ing yon - der pin - nace on!
Wie?
See!
Ein Schwan zieht ei - nen
A fair swan lead - ing
Wie?
See!
Wie?
See!
(The Second Chorus consists of those more remote from the water, who anxiously question, without quitting their places, those who are behind them; later they severally go to the back to see for themselves.)
TENOR I.
Wie?
What!
TENOR II.
2nd Chorus.
BASS I.
BASS II.

(One.)
(All.)
Ein Rit-ter drin! Ein Rit-ter drin hoch
And lo, a knight! A war-rior full fair,
Na-chen dort her-an!
yon-der pin-nace on!
Ha!
Ha!
Wie?
What?
Was ist?
What is't?
Wie?
What?

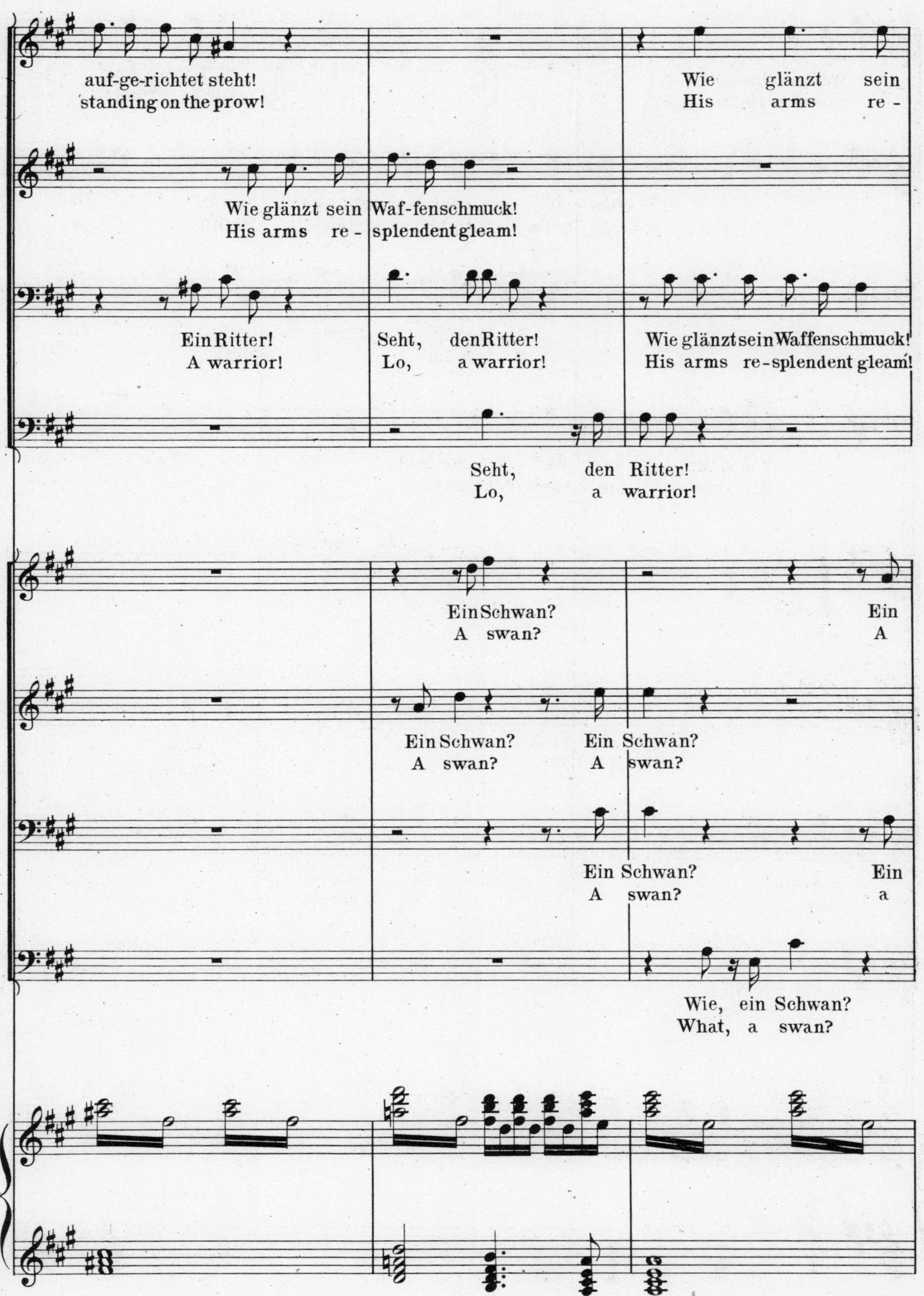
auf-ge-richtet steht!
standing on the prow!
Wie glänzt sein
His arms re-
Wie glänzt sein Waf-fenschmuck!
His arms re-splendent gleam!
Ein Ritter!
A warrior!
Seht, den Ritter!
Lo, a warrior!
Wie glänzt sein Waffenschmuck!
His arms re-splendent gleam!
Seht, den Ritter!
Lo, a warrior!
Ein Schwan?
A swan?
Ein
A
Ein Schwan?
A swan?
Ein Schwan?
A swan?
Ein Schwan?
A swan?
Ein
a
Wie, ein Schwan?
What, a swan?

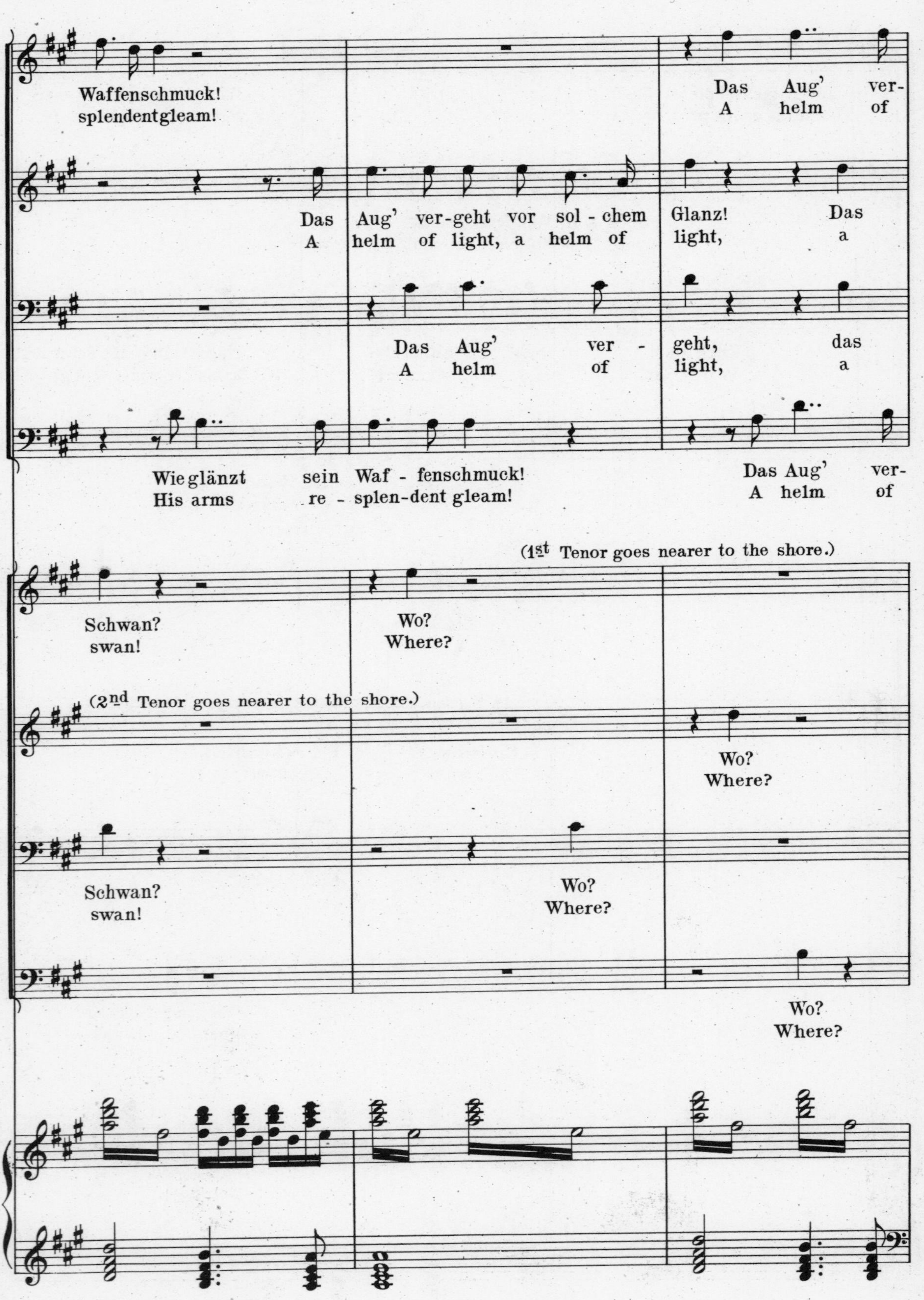
Waffenschmuck!
splendentgleam!
Das Aug' ver-
A helm of
Das Aug' ver-geht vor sol - chem Glanz! Das
A helm of light, a helm of light, a
Das Aug' ver - geht, das
A helm of light, a
Wie glänzt sein Waf - fenschmuck!
His arms re - splen-dent gleam!
Das Aug' ver-
A helm of
(1st Tenor goes nearer to the shore.)
Schwan?
swan!
Wo?
Where?
(2nd Tenor goes nearer to the shore.)
Wo?
Where?
Schwan?
swan!
Wo?
Where?
Wo?
Where?

geht vor sol - chem Glanz!
light up-on his brow!
Aug' vergeht vor dem Glanz!
helm of light on his brow!
Aug' vergeht vor dem Glanz!
helm of light on his brow!
geht vor sol - chem Glanz!
light up - on his brow!
Seht, nä - her kommt er
See, now the shore he
Ei-nen Na - chen zieht er her - an!
See, a swan leads yon pin-nace on!
Ei-nen Na - chen zieht er her - an!
See, a swan leads yon pin-nace on!
(1st Bass goes to the shore.)
Vor ei - nem Na-chen?
Where's yon - der pin-nace?
Ei-nen Na-chen? Wen führt er?
How a pin-nace? Who is it?
fp

(Here a bend of the river conceals Lohengrin from view, *R. H.*; the performers, however, can see him from the stage.)

Seht! seht! dort! Immer nä - her,—
Look! look! there! He comes near - er,—
Seht! seht! dort! Immer nä - her,—
Look! look! there! He comes near - er,—
Seht, nä-her kommt er an!
Look, he hath gain'd the shore!
an! Seht! dort! Seht, immer nä - her
gains! Look! there! Look, he hath gain'd the
Einen Rit-ter! Seht! seht! Ein
'Tis a war-rior! Look! look! A
Einen Rit-ter! Seht! seht! Ein
'Tis a war-rior! Look! look! A
Ein Rit - ter drin naht dem Strand; seht,
A knight with-in gains the shore, look,
(2nd Bass hastens to the shore.)
Wie? Was?
Where? What?

seht! kommt er schon her - an!
look! he hath gain'd the shore!
An ei-ner gold' - nen
And with a chain of
seht! kommt er schon her - an! Seht, immer nä - her kommt er schon her-
look! he hath gain'd the shore! Look, he comes near - er, he hath gain'd the
Seht! Näher kommt er an! Seht, immer nä - her kommt er schon her-
Look! he hath gain'd the shore! Look, he comes near - er, he hath gain'd the
kommt er schon her - an!
shore! he comes, he comes!
Rit - ter_ und ein Schwan! Welch' selt - sam Wun - der! Seht!
war-rior_ and a swan! This is a mar - vel! Look!
Rit - ter_ und ein Schwan! Welch' selt - sam Wun - der! Seht!
war-rior_ and a swan! This is a mar - vel! Look!
nä - her kommt er an! Welch' selt - sam Wun - der! Seht!
look, he gains the shore! This is a mar - vel! Look!
Wahrlich, ein Rit-ter ist's! Welch' selt - sam
Tru-ly, it is a knight! This is a
cresc.

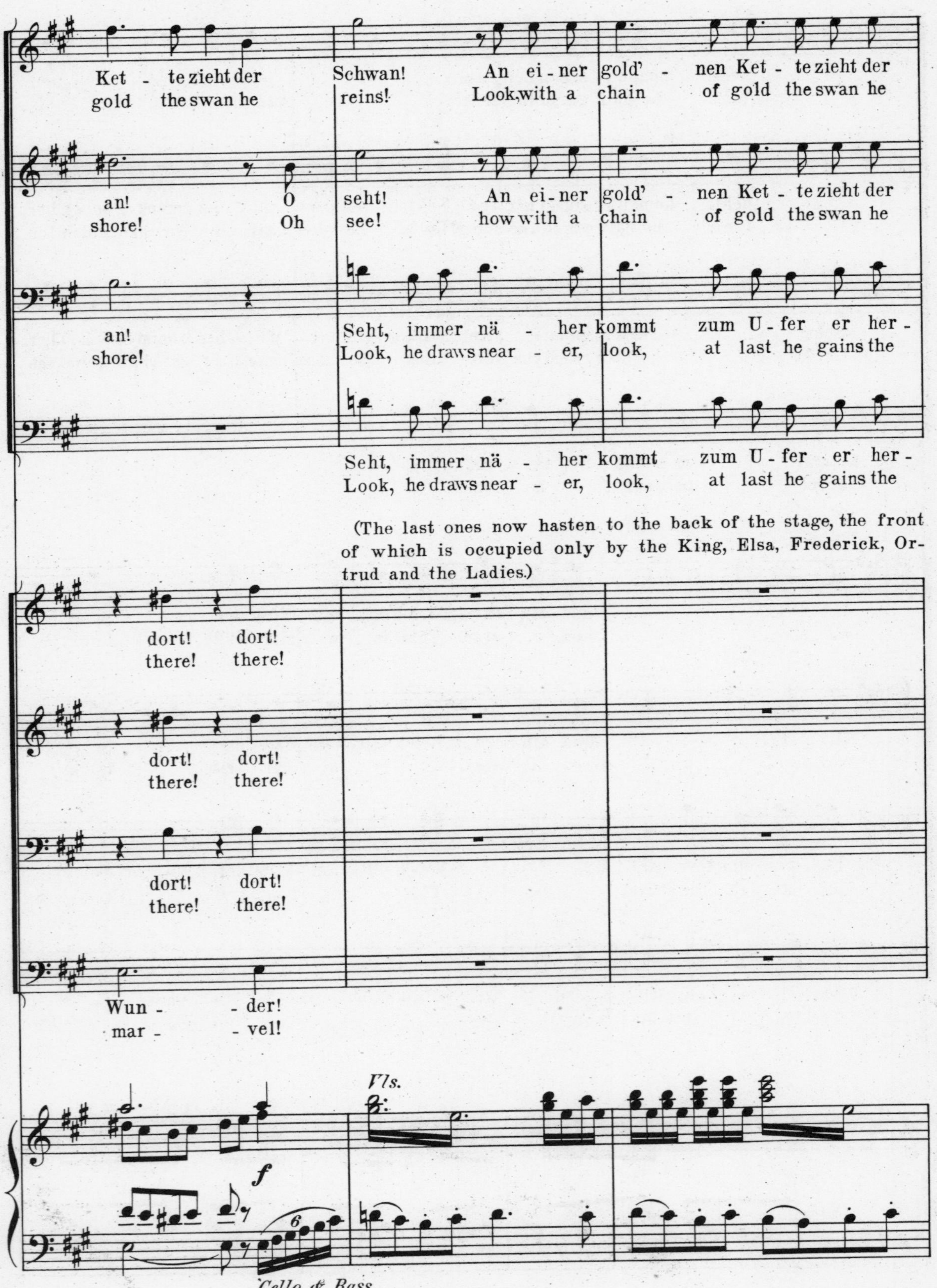
Ket - te zieht der
gold the swan he
Schwan!
reins!
An ei-ner gold' - nen Ket - te zieht der
Look, with a chain of gold the swan he
an!
shore!
O
Oh
seht!
see!
An ei-ner gold' - nen Ket - te zieht der
how with a chain of gold the swan he
Seht, immer nä - her kommt zum U-fer er her-
Look, he draws near - er, look, at last he gains the
Seht, immer nä - her kommt zum U-fer er her-
Look, he draws near - er, look, at last he gains the
(The last ones now hasten to the back of the stage, the front of which is occupied only by the King, Elsa, Frederick, Ortrud and the Ladies.)
dort! dort!
there! there!
dort! dort!
there! there!
dort! dort!
there! there!
Wun - der!
mar - vel!
Vls.
Cello & Bass.

TENOR I & II. 1st Chorus.
Schwan!
reins!
Seht hin! Er naht!
Be-hold, he comes!
BASS I & II.
an!
shore!
Seht hin! Er naht!
Be-hold, he comes!
2nd Chorus.
TENOR I & II.
An ei-ner gold'-nen Ket-te zieht der Schwan!
And with a chain of gold the swan he reins!
BASS I & II.
Seht, im-mer nä-her kommt zum U-fer er her-an!
Look, he hath gain'd the shore, he now hath gain'd the shore!
più f
(In great excitement all rush to the front.) Both Choruses of Men.
Seht, er naht!
Lo, he comes!
Ein
A
Seht hin! Er naht Seht, er naht!
Be-hold, he comes! Lo, he comes!
Ein
A
Seht hin! Er naht
Be-hold, he comes!
12946

(The King, from his raised seat, sees all that passes; Frederick and Ortrud are petrified with surprise and dread; Elsa, who has listened to the exclamations of the men with growing transports, remains in her place in the centre of the stage, not daring to look around.)

The Ladies (falling on their knees.)
SOPRANO and ALTO.

ff

Dank, _____ du
Thanks, _____ oh

ff

Wun - - der! Ein Wun - der, ein
mar - - vel! A mar - vel, a

ff

nie _____ ge - seh'nes Wun - der, ein
mar - - vel, yes, a mar - vel, a

ff

Ped. *

Herr _____ und Gott, der _____
gra - - cious Lord, Thou _____

ff

Wun - der, ein Wun - der ist ge - kom-men, ein un - er-
mar - vel, a mar - vel wrought a - mongst us, a great, un-

ff

Wun - der, ein Wun - der ist ge - kom-men, ein un - er-
mar - vel, a mar - vel wrought a - mongst us, a great, un-

(All here turn their eyes expectantly to the back of the stage.)

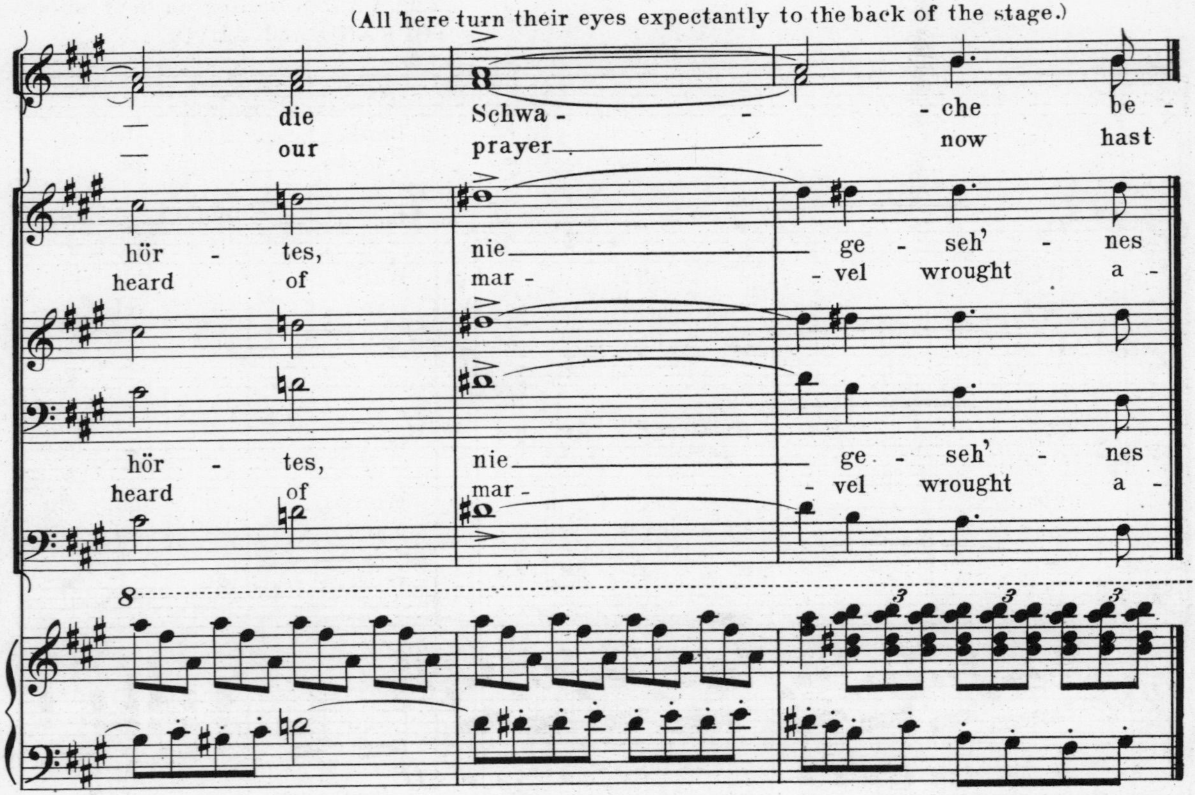

Scene III.

(Here the skiff, drawn by the swan, reaches the shore in the centre at the back of the stage; Lohengrin, in a silver coat of mail, with a shining helmet, his shield at his back, a little golden horn at his side, stands within it, leaning on his sword. Frederick gazes on Lohengrin in speechless amazement. Ortrud, who during the preceding had preserved a cold and haughty bearing, is seized by terrible consternation at the sight of the swan. All deferentially bare their heads.)

1 Piccolo, 2 Flutes, 3 Oboes, 3 Cls. in A, 3 Bassoons, Horns in E and A, 3 Trumpets in E, 3 Trombones, Bass Tuba, Kettle-Drum in A and E, Cymbals and Strings.

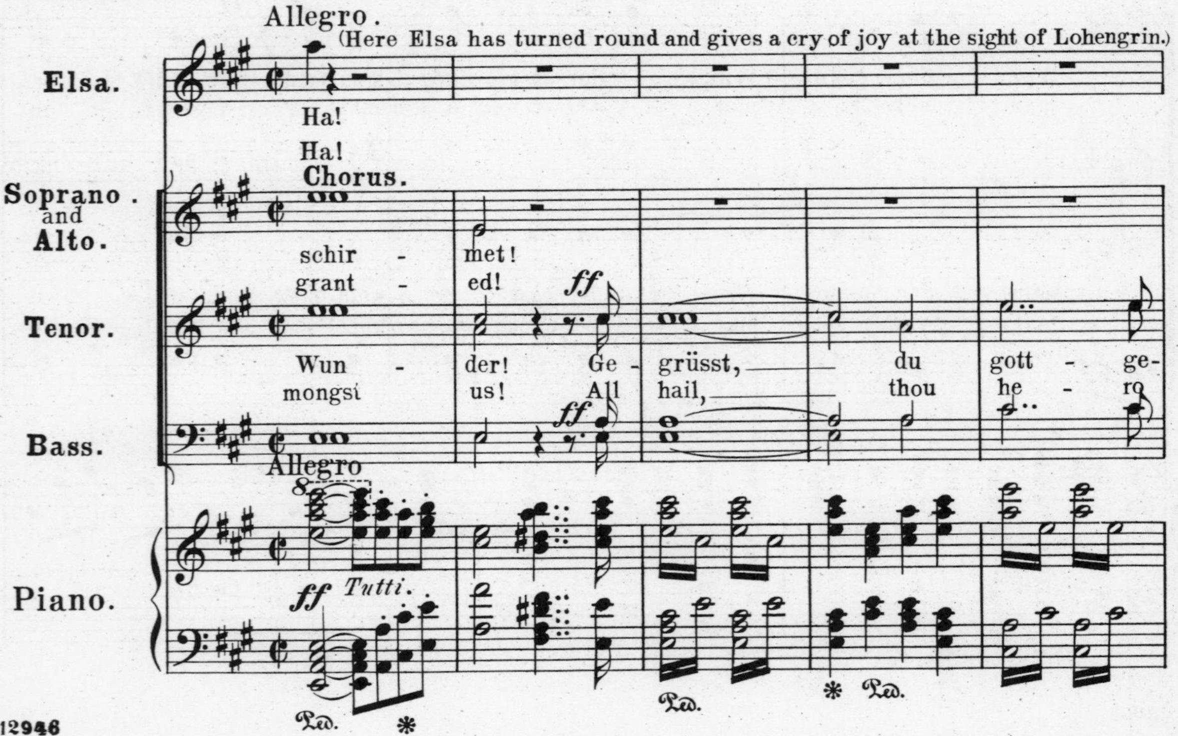

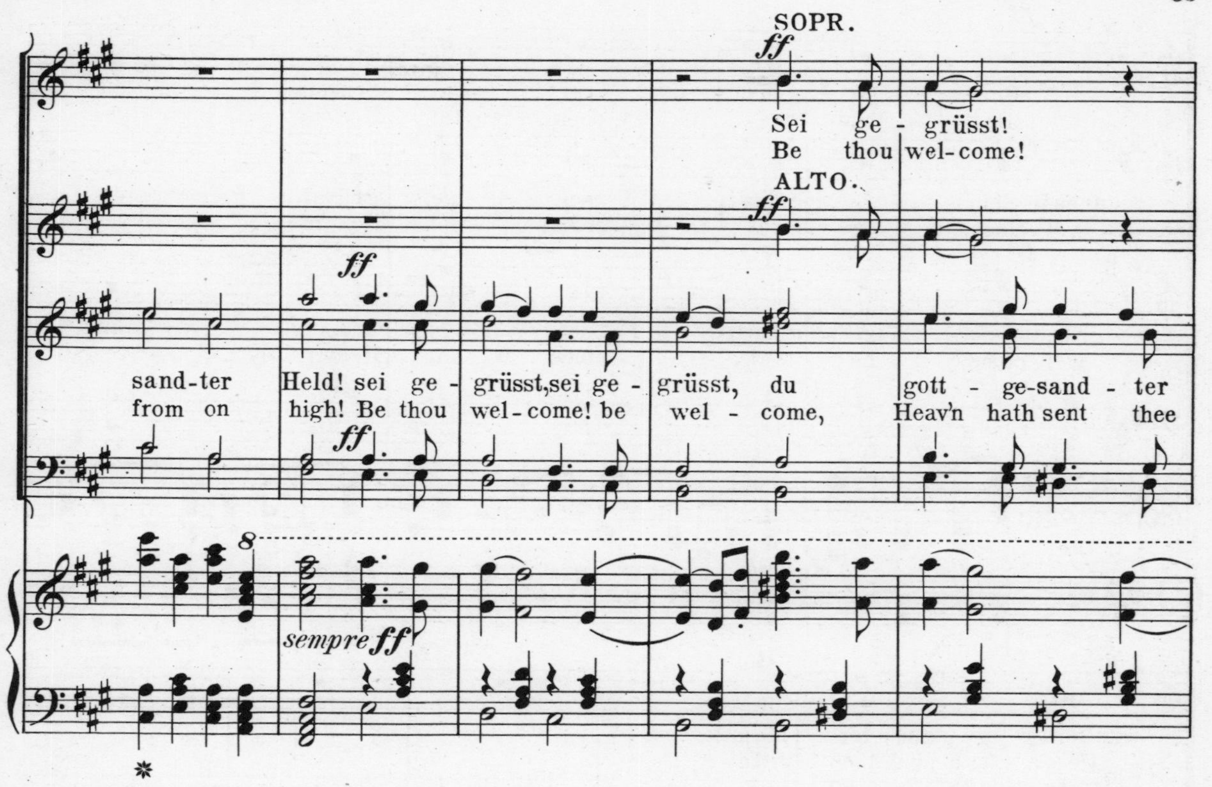

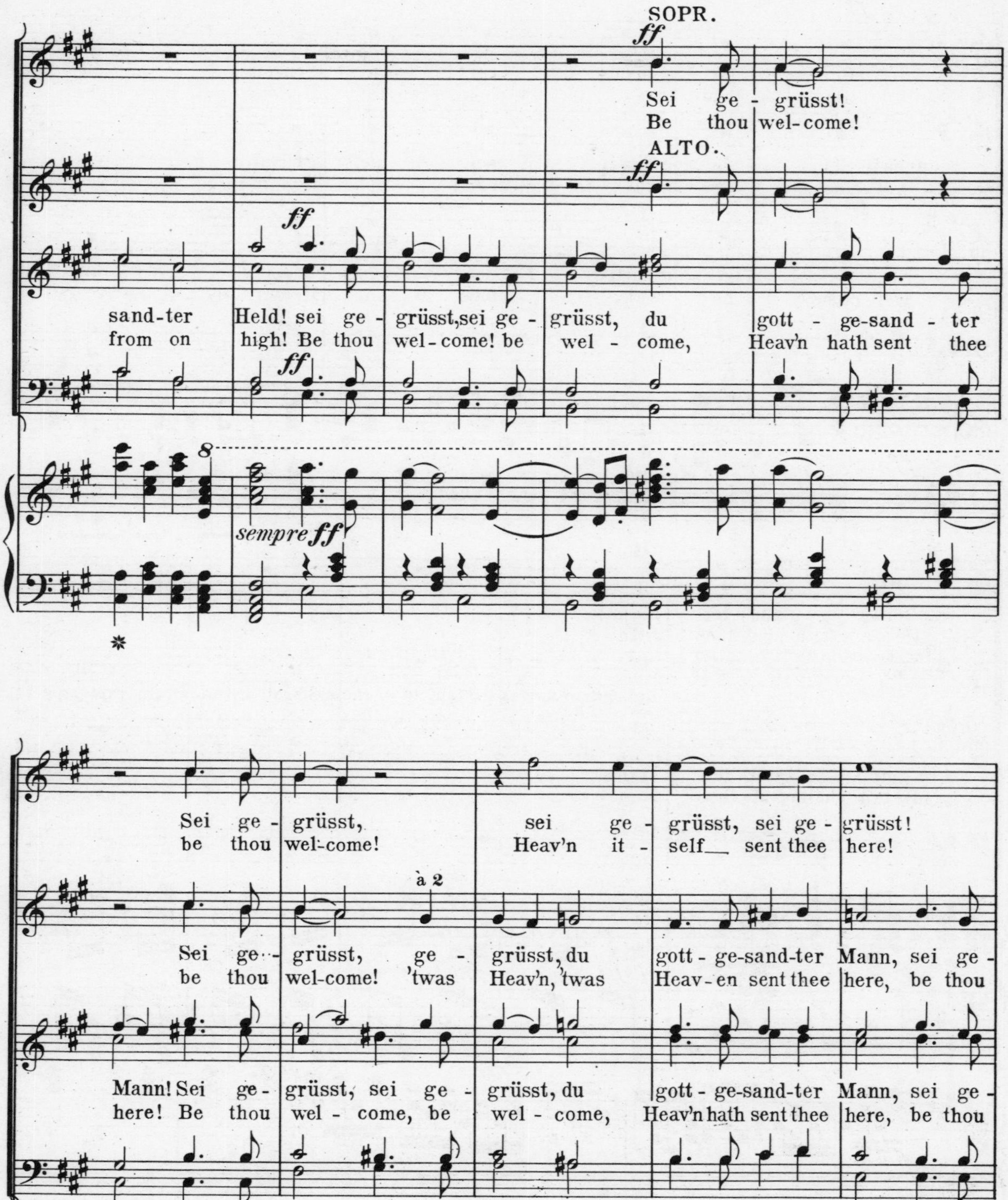

SOPR.
ff
Sei ge - grüsst!
Be thou wel-come!
ALTO.
ff
ff
sand-ter Held! sei ge - grüsst, sei ge - grüsst, du gott - ge-sand - ter
from on high! Be thou wel-come! be wel - come, Heav'n hath sent thee
ff
8
sempre ff
Sei ge - grüsst, sei ge - grüsst, sei ge - grüsst!
be thou wel-come! Heav'n it - self sent thee here!
à 2
Sei ge - grüsst, ge - grüsst, du gott - ge-sand-ter Mann, sei ge -
be thou wel-come! 'twas Heav'n, 'twas Heav - en sent thee here, be thou
Mann! Sei ge - grüsst, sei ge - grüsst, du gott - ge-sand-ter Mann, sei ge -
here! Be thou wel - come, be wel - come, Heav'n hath sent thee here, be thou
8

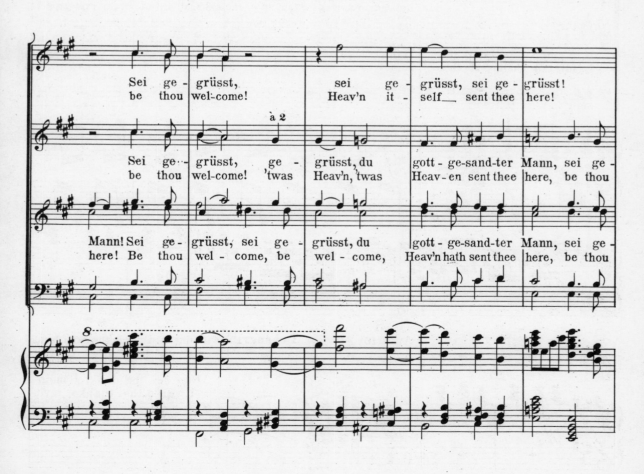

ff
Sei ge-grüsst, sei ge-grüsst, du
Be thou wel-come, for Heav'n, yes,
grüsst! Sei ge-grüsst, sei ge-grüsst, du
wel-come, be wel-come, for Heav'n, yes,
Tpts., K.-Dr. & Trombs.
gott-ge-sand-ter Mann!
Heav'n hath sent thee here!
(As Lohengrin moves to step out of the skiff, all are silent, in rapt expectancy.)
Tutti.
dim.
piu p
3 Fl.
Adagio.
Lohengrin. (with one foot still in the skiff, bends
Nun sei be-dankt, mein
I give thee thanks, my
Vls. only.
pp
rit.
dim.

toward the swan.)
lie - ber Schwan! Zieh' durch die wei - te Fluth zu-rück da - hin, wo-her mich
trusty swan! Turn thee a - gain and breast the tide, re - turn un - to that
Vls.
pp
trug dein Kahn, kehr' wie-der nur zu un - serm Glück! Drum sei ge - treu dein
land of dawn, where late we did in joy a - bide! Well thy ap - point-ed
(The swan slowly turns the skiff and swims back on the stream; Lohengrin sorrowfully looks after it for some time.)
Dienst ge-than! Leb' wohl! Leb' wohl! mein lie - ber Schwan!
task is done! Fare-well! fare-well, my trust-y swan!
Ob. Cl. Cor. Ingl.
Chorus.
SOPR. (as delicately as possible.)
ALTO.
Wie fasst uns se - lig sü - sses Grauen, welch' hol - de
Doth he not seem from Heav'n de-scended? His ra - diant
1st TENOR. (in falsetto.)
2nd TENOR.
Wie fasst uns se - lig Grau - en!
He seems from Heav'n de - scend - ed!
1st BASS.
Wie fasst uns se - lig Grau - en, was
He seems from Heav'n de - scend - ed! His
2nd BASS.
Wie fasst uns se - lig Grau - en, welch' hol - de
He seems from Heav'n de - scen - ed! His ra - diant
'Cello.

Here Lohengrin leaves the bank, and slowly advances towards the front.

hehr!
fair!
Wie schön!
How fair!
schön und hehr zu schau-en, den solch' ein Wun-der trug an's Land!
grace in him are blend-ed, to deeds of glo-ry he is call'd!
schön und hehr zu schau-en, den solch' ein Wun-der trug an's Land!
grace in him are blend-ed, to deeds of glo-ry he is call'd!
solch' ein Wun - der uns trug an's Land!
deeds of glo - ry by Heav'n he's call'd!
schön, den die-ses Wun - der trug an's Land!
fair, he is to deeds of glo - ry call'd!
-en, den solch' Wun-der trug an's Land!
-ed, to glo - ry by Heav'n he's call'd!
3 Tpts.
Lohengrin.
(Lohengrin makes his obeisance to the King.)
Heil, Kö-nig Heinrich! Se-gen-voll mög
Hail, gra-cious sov'reign! Vic-to-ry and
Wind.
Gott bei dei-nem Schwerte stehn! Ruhm-reich und gross dein Na-me
hon-or be thy val-or's meed! Thy glo-rious name shall from the
Tpts.
cresc.

The King.
soll von die-ser Er-de nie ver-geh'n!
land that chose thee ruler, ne'er de-part!
Hab' Dank! Erkenn' ich
Have thanks! me-thinks I
p
f
p dolce.
Str.
'Cello.
p
recht die Macht, die dich in die-ses Land ge-bracht, so nahst du uns von
know the Pow'r that sent thee here in this dread hour; On Heav-en's mis-sion
più p
Lohengrin.
Gott ge-sandt?
thou art come.
Zum Kampf für ei-ne
I came for yonder
Vl. only.
pp
Fl.
pp
p
B. Cl.
Magd zu steh'n, der schwe-re Kla-ge an-ge-than, bin ich ge-sandt, nun lasst mich
maid to fight, from dark surmise her name to clear, in quarrel true to guard her
p
dim.
(He draws nearer to Elsa.)
seh'n, ob ich zurecht sie tref-fe an!
right, who now my proffer'd vow shall hear!
So sprich denn, El-sa von Bra-
I ask thee, El-sa of Bra-
pp
pp
Tpts.
Wind.
p

bant, Wenn ich zum Streiter dir er-nannt, willst du wohl oh-ne Bang' und
bant, if thou the boon to me wilt grant, as thy champion to fight this
(Elsa, who has remained spellbound since she perceived Lohengrin, roused by his address and
Poco più mosso.
Elsa.
Grau'n dich meinem Schut-ze an-ver-trau'n? Mein Held, mein
day, wilt thou en-trust thy cause to me? My hope, my
Ob.
ff
p
overwhelmed with rapturous emotion, sinks on her knees before him.)
Adagio.
Ret-ter! Nimm mich hin! Dir geb' ich Al-les, was ich bin!
solace, he-ro mine! Do thou pro-tect me, I am thine!
f
fp
p
p
Wood.
Lohegrin. (with great fervor.)
Wenn ich im Kam-pfe für dich sie-ge,
If in thy cause to-day I con-quer,
f
p
Str.
dim.
Elsa.
willst du, dass ich dein Gat-te sei? Wie ich zu dei-nen
wilt thou enpledge thy faith to me? As here I low-ly
Ob.
più p
p
p

Fü - ssen lie - ge, geb' ich dir Leib und See - le frei.
bend be - fore_thee, thine will I now and ev - er be.
p
Fl.
più p
Lohengrin.
El - sa, soll ich dein Gat - te hei - ssen, soll_Land und Leut' ich
El - sa, if thou thy troth_wilt plight me, if_from the foe_ this
Str. sempre pp
schir - men dir, soll nichts_ mich wie - der von dir rei - ssen, musst
land_ I save, if naught_ from me shall dis - u - nite_ thee, a
Very slowly.
Ei - nes du ge - lo - ben mir. Nie sollst du mich be - fra - gen,
promise I of thee must crave. Nev - er, as thou dost love me,
f
p
più p
Ob. & Cl.
Bssn.
noch Wis - sen's Sor - ge tra - gen, wo - her ich kam der Fahrt, noch wie mein
aught shall to question move thee, from whence to thee I came, or what my
pp
Wind.

Elsa (softy, almost unconsciously.)
Lohengrin. (with
Nam' und Art! Nie, Herr, soll mir die Fra - ge kommen! El - sa!
race and name! Lord, at thy will thou shalt com-mand me! El - sa!
pp
Strgs.
raised voice, very earnestly.)
(more decisively.)
Hast du mich wohl ver - nom-men? Nie sollst du mich be - fra - gen,
Say, dost thou un - der - stand me? Nev - er, as thou dost love me,
Ob.
Vl.
Fl.& Cl.
Bassn.
noch Wissen's Sor - ge tra - gen, wo - her ich kam der Fahrt, noch wie mein Nam' und
aught shall to question move thee, from whence to thee I came, or what my race and
Wind
più
Elsa (looking up to him with intense devotion.)
Art! Mein Schirm! Mein Engel! Mein Er - lö - ser, der fest an meine
name! Oh thou! my he - ro, my de - fend - er, no doubt of me is
Molto tranquillo.
Wood.
Unschuld glaubt! Wie gäb' es Zwei - fels Schuld, die grö - sser, als die an
in thy heart, I life and faith to thee sur - ren - der, how could I

dich — den Glau-ben raubt? Wie du mich schirmst in mei-ner
ques - tion what thou art? As thou wilt guard my name and
Noth, so — halt' in Treu' ich — dein Ge-bot!
land, thus — will I cher-ish — thy com-mand!
Str.
Lohengrin (raising Elsa to his heart.)
El - sa! Ich lie-be dich!
El - sa, I worship thee!
Chorus (softly, with emotion.)
SOPRANO.
ALTO.
TENOR I.
Welch' hol - de
Oh sweet en-
TENOR II.
BASS I.
Welch' hol - de
Oh sweet en-
BASS II.
Welch'
Oh
Tutti (Str. trem.)
cresc.
p Wind.
sempre

(Elsa and Lohengrin remain for some moments embraced.)

pp

Welch' hol - de Wun - der! Ist's Zau - ber, der mir
Oh sweet en - chant - ment! some mag - ic pow'r my

Wun - der! Ist's Zau - ber, der mir an - ge -
chant-ment! oh sweet en - chant-ment, won - drous

pp

Welch' hol - de Wun - der!
Oh sweet en - chant-ment!

Wun - der! Welch' hol - de Wun - der muss ich
chant-ment! oh sweet en - chant - ment, won-drous

Wun - der muss ich seh'n?
sweet and won - drous love!

pp

(Lohengrin leads Elsa to the King and gives her into his care.)

pp

Ich fühl' das Her - ze mir ver-geh'n, schau' ich den
Deep in my heart thy spell I prove, splen - dor di -

dolce.

an - ge - than? Ich fühl' das Herz mir ver - ge -
sens - es sways, oh wondrous love, sweet en - chant -

dolce.

than? Ich fühl' das Herz mir ver - geh'n,
love! oh wondrous love, won - drous love,

pp

Ich fühl' das Herz, ich fühl' das Herz mir ver - geh'n,
Thy spell I prove, *dolce.* oh wondrous love, won - drous love,

seh'n! Ich füh - le das Herz mir ver - geh'n,
love! Thy spell now I prove, won - drous love,

pp

Ich fühl' mir das Herz ver -
some mag - ic my sens - es

pp
won - ne-vol-len Mann! Schau'
vine a-round them plays! Splen -
hen, Ich fühl' das Herz mir ver- ge - hen,
ment, Oh won-drous love, sweet en - chant - ment,
pp pp
schau' ich den heh-ren Mann, ich fühl' das Herz mir ver-
thy spell, oh won-drous love, oh love, thou mag-ic-al
pp pp
schau' ich den heh-ren Mann, ich fühl' das Herz ver -
thy spell, oh won-drous love, thy spell thou mag - ic
pp pp
schau' ich den heh-ren Mann, ich fühl' das Herz mir ver -
thy spell, oh won-drous love, thy spell, oh love, now I
geh'n, schau' ich den heh - - ren Mann,
sways, deep in my heart I prove
pp
ich den heh - ren, won-ne-vol-len Mann!
dor di-vine a-round their tress-es plays!
schau' ich den won-ne-vol-len Mann!
a light di-vine a-round them plays!
ge-hen, schau' ich den won-ne-vol-len Mann!
pow-er, splen-dor di-vine a-round them plays!
ge-hen, schau' ich den heh - ren Mann!
pow-er, splen-dor a-round them plays!
ge-hen, schau' ich den heh - ren Mann!
prove, splen-dor a-round them plays!
schau' ich den heh - ren Mann!
thy spell, oh won - d'rous love!
p

(Lohengrin solemnly steps into the midst of the circle) Lohengrin.
Nun hört!
Ye knights,
Tpts.
cresc.
fp
Trombs.
Euch, Volk und Ed-len, mach' ich kund: frei al-ler Schuld is El-sa von Bra-
no-bles and free-men of this land, guilt-less and true is El-sa of Bra-
fp
fp
bant! Dass falsch dein Kla-gen, Graf von
bant! Thy tale was false-hood, Count of
Str.
f
ff
K.-Dr.
p
Tel-ra-mund, durch Got-tes Ur-theil werd' es dir be-
Tel-ra-mund, by Heav'n's as-sistance all_thou shalt re-
Wind.
5
6
f
f
ff
ff

Allegro.
kannt!
cant!
Two 1st TENORS.
Two 2nd TENORS.
Steh' ab! Steh'
Re-frain, the
Two 1st BASSES.
Steh' ab vom Kampf! Wenn du ihn wagst, zu sie-gen
Re-frain, re-frain, The fight for-go, thou wilt but
Two 1st BASSES. Steh' ab vom Kampf!
Three 2d BASSES. Re-frain, re-frain!
Steh' ab vom Kampf!
Re-frain, re-frain!
Two 2nd BASSES.
Allegro.
pp Tnr., 'Cello, Cl. & Bassn.
ab vom Kampf! Steh'
fight for-go! This
nim-mer du ver-magst. Ist er von höch-ster Macht be-
win dis-tress and woe. If it is Heav'n that sent him
Wa-ge ihn nicht! Ist er von
Oh be ad-vis'd! If it is
Lass ab vom Kampf! Ist er von
Oh be ad-vis'd! If it is
Hör' un-sern Rath!
Oh be ad-vis'd!

ab! Hör'
fight, for -
p
schützt, sag', was dein tapf' - res Schwert dir
here, what will a - vail thy sword or
p
höch - ster Macht be - schützt, sag', was dein
Heav'n that sent him here, what will a -
höch - ster Macht be - schützt, sag', was dein
Heav'n that sent him here, what will a -
Steh' ab vom Kampf!
this fight for - go!
3
f p
uns! Steh' ab vom Kampf!
go! Re - frain, re - frain!
f p
nützt? Steh' ab vom Kampf! Wir mah - nen dich in
spear? Re - frain, re - frain! I warn thee as a
f p
Schwert dir nützt? Steh' ab vom
vail thy sword? Oh be ad -
f p
Schwert dir nützt? Steh' ab vom
vail thy sword? Oh be ad -
f
Wag' ihn' nicht! Steh'
Go not forth to -
pp 3

p
accel. cresc.
Wir mah - nen dich in Treu'! Dein har - ret
I warn thee as a friend, or in dis -
p
Treu'! Dein har - ret Un - sieg,
friend, or in dis - as - ter
p
cresc.
Kampf, wir mah - nen dich in Treu'! Dein har - ret
vis'd, I warn thee as a friend! Or in dis -
p
Kampf, wir mah - nen dich in Treu'! Dein har - ret
vis'd, I warn thee as a friend! Or in dis -
Four 2nd BASSES.
p
ab! Dein har - ret Un - sieg,
day, Or in dis - as - ter
accel.
pp
cresc.
f
Un - sieg, bit - t're Reu'!
as - ter thou wilt end!
Four BASSES.
f
bit - t're Reu'!
thou wilt end!
f
Un - sieg, bit - t're Reu'!
as - ter thou wilt end!
f
Un - sieg, bit - t're Reu'!
as - ter thou wilt end!
f
bit - t're Reu'!
thou wilt end!
f Str.

Frederick, (who has been gazing fixedly and intently at Lohengrin) vehemently.
Viel lie - ber todt, als feig!
If I must fail, I'll die!
più f
ff
6
sempre ff 2nd Vl. & Tnr.
Welch' Zau - bern dich auch her - ge -
What spells so - e'er have brought thee
führt, Fremd - ling, der mir so kühn er -
here, Stran - ger, who dost my sword de -
scheint, dein stol - zes Droh'n mich nim - mer
fy, No cause have I thy threats to
rührt, da ich zu lü - gen nie ver -
fear, for all is truth my words im -

meint: den Kampf mit dir drum nehm' ich
ply: behold me pre - par'd for the
auf, und hof - fe
fray, if right pre -
più f
Sieg nach Rech - - tes
vails, I'll win the
ff
ff
Lohengrin.
Lauf! Nun, Kö - nig, or -
day! Great sov - 'reign, now
Tpts & Tromb.
Str.
f
p
cresc.
Wind.
f
(All resume the places they were in when the Council began.)
- d'ne un-sern Kampf!
or-dain the fight!
Tutti.
ff

The King.

So tre-tet vor, zu drei für je-den Kämpfer, und mes-set wohl den Ring zum Streite ab!

Up-on each side three knights the space shall measure, I here proclaim this place a fenced field.

f Str. *f* *poco rit.* *p* *poco meno mosso.* *Trombs.* *p ma marcato e stacc.* *D. Bass & Bassn.*

(Three Saxon Nobles advance for Lohengrin, and three Brabantians for Frederick; they cross the stage with solemn strides and measure the ground for the combat; when the six have formed a complete circle they drive their spears into the ground.)

tr *p* *cresc.* *tr* *f* *dim.* *p* *ff* *Ped.* *

Herald. (in the centre of the ring.)

All the Men.

ff

Der Frei - e büss' ___ es mit der
The Free-man straight ___ shall lose his

ff *ff*

Hand,' mit sei-nem Haup - te büss' es der
hand, and his base head shall for - feit the

f *dim.*

Herald.

Hört auch, ihr Strei - ter vor Ge -
Mark me, ye com - ba - tants of

Knecht!
thrall!

Tromb. & Tpts.

p *p* *Str.* *tr* *tr*

richt! Ge - wahrt in Treu - e Kam - pfes
might. In fair and o - pen quar - rel

Tpts. & Trombs.

ff *p*

Pflicht! Durch bö-sen Zau-bers List und Trug stört nicht des
fight! By mag-ic arts ye shall not win, that were the
Str.
Tpts. & Trombs.
Ur-theils Ei-gen-schaft! Gott rich-tet euch nach Recht und Fug,—
judgment to de-ride! Pros-per, as free ye are from sin,
Wind.
dim.
so trau-et ihm, nicht eu-rer Kraft!
not in your-selves, in Heav'n con-fide!
Tpts.
cresc.
(Both stand outside the circle, on different sides.)
Lohengrin.
Gott rich-te mich nach Recht und Fug!— So trau' ich ihm, nicht mei-ner
Judge me, as free I am from sin! Not in my-self, in Heav'n I
Frederick.
Gott rich-te mich nach Recht und Fug!— So trau' ich ihm,— nicht mei-ner
Judge me, as free I am from sin! Not in my-self,— in Heav'n I
Brass.

Kraft!
bide!
The King. (solemnly.)
(The King steps into the centre.)
Kraft!
bide!
Mein Herr und Gott,
Oh King of kings,
Tutti.
ritard.
ff
ff Wind.
(Here all bare their heads, and listen devoutly.)
nun ruf' ich dich, dass du dem Kampf zu - ge - gen sei'st! Durch
on Thee I call; look down on us in this dread hour! Let
lunga.
Tromb. & Tpts.
ff
pp
Schwer-tes Sieg ein Ur-theil sprich, das Trug und Wahrheit
Him in this or - de - al fall whom Thou know'st guil-ty,
p
cresc.
mf
dim.
klar- er-weist! Des Rei-nen Arm gieb Hel-den-kraft, des
Lord of pow'r! To stain-less knight give strength and might, with
p
p

Fal - schen Stär - ke sei er - schlafft: so hilf uns,
cra - ven heart the false one smite: do Thou, O
fp
mf
Gott, zu die - ser Frist, weil un - s're Weis - heit Ein - falt
Lord, to hear us deign, for all our wis - dom is but
f
dim.
p
più p
Elsa.
p
Du kün - dest nun dein
Now, Lord, make known Thy
Ortrud.
p
Ich bau - e
In his strong
Lohengrin.
p
Du kün - dest nun dein
Now, Lord, make known Thy
Frederick.
p
ritard.
ist, weil un - s're Weisheit Ein - falt ist!
vain, for all our wisdom is but vain.
ritard.
Hns.
più p
pp
p

f dim. p

wahr Ge - richt, mein Gott und Herr, drum zag' ich
just de - cree, I have no fear, I trust in

f dim. p

fest auf sei - ne Kraft, die, wo er kämpft, ihm Sieg ver-
arm I trust a - lone, that nor de - feat nor fear hath

f dim. p

wahr Ge - richt, mein Gott und Herr, drum zag' ich
just de - cree, I have no fear, I trust in

f dim. p

Ich geh' in Treu' vor dein Ge - richt!
I here a - wait Thy just de - cree;

f

p p

nicht! Du kün - dest nun dein wahr Ge - richt:
Thee! Now, Lord, make known Thy just de - cree,

p p

schafft. Ich bau - e fest auf sei - ne Kraft,
known, In his strong arm I trust a - lone,

p p

nicht! Du kün - dest nun dein wahr Ge - richt:
Thee! Now, Lord, make known Thy just de - cree, *molto*

p p

Herr Gott! Herr Gott, nun ver-
Great Lord, Lord, let not my

p p

Mein Herr und Gott, dich ru - fe ich!
Oh King of kings, on Thee I call!

Mein Herr und Gott, drum zag' ich
I have no fear, I trust in
die, wo er kämpft, ihm Sieg ver-
that nor de-feat nor fear hath
espress.
Mein Gott, drum zag' ich
I have no fear, no
lass mein' Eh-re nicht, ver-lass mein' Eh-re
hon-or tar-nish'd be, let not my hon-or,
Nun künd' uns, nun
Oh hear us now,
nicht, mein Gott, drum zag' ich nicht!
Thee, oh Lord, I trust in Thee.
schafft.
known.
nicht, drum nun zag' ich nicht!
fear, for I trust in Thee!
nicht, ver-lass mein' Eh-re nicht!
not my hon-or tar-nish'd be!
kün-de uns dein wahr Ge-richt!
Lord, make known Thy just de-cree!
Mein Herr und
Oh King of
TENOR.
All the Men.
BASS. Herald with BASS I.
Des Rei-nen Arm gieb
To stain-less Knight give
cresc.
Hns. & Bssn. Str. pizz.

Ich bau - e
In his strong
Du kün - dest nun dein wahr Ge -
Now, Lord, make known, oh Lord, make
Ich geh' in Treu' vor dein Ge - richt, Herr Gott, ver - lass mein'
I here a - wait Thy just de - cree, let not my hon - or
Gott, dich ru - fe jetzt ich an, dass du dem
kings, on Thee I call, look down, look down on
SOPRANO.
The Ladies.
ALTO.
Hel - den kraft, des Fal - schen Stär - ke sei er -
strength and might, with cra - ven heart the false one

Mein Herr, o mein Gott!
Oh hear, gra - cious Lord,
fest auf sei - ne Kraft, auf sei - ne Kraft.
arm, in his strong arm I trust a - lone.
richt, dein wahr Ge - richt! Mein
known Thy just de - cree! My
Eh - re nicht, Herr Gott, Herr Gott, ver -
tar - nish'd be, great Lord, great Lord, Let
Kampf zu - ge - gen sei'st! Durch Schwertes
us in this dread hour! Let him in
Mein Herr und Gott!
My gra - cious Lord!
schlafft:
smite,
so hilf uns Gott, zu
do thou, O Lord, to

Du kün - dest
Now make Thou
Ich bau - e fest auf sei - ne Kraft, die,
In his strong arm I trust a - lone, that
Gott, drum zag' ich nicht, drum
Lord, I have no fear, I
lass, ver - lass, ver - lass mein' Eh - re
not, let not my hon - or tar - nish'd
Sieg sprich dein Ur - theil, das Trug und
this day's or - deal fall, whom Thou know'st
die - ser Frist, weil un - s're Weis - heit
hear us deign, for all our wis - dom
p
dim.
fp

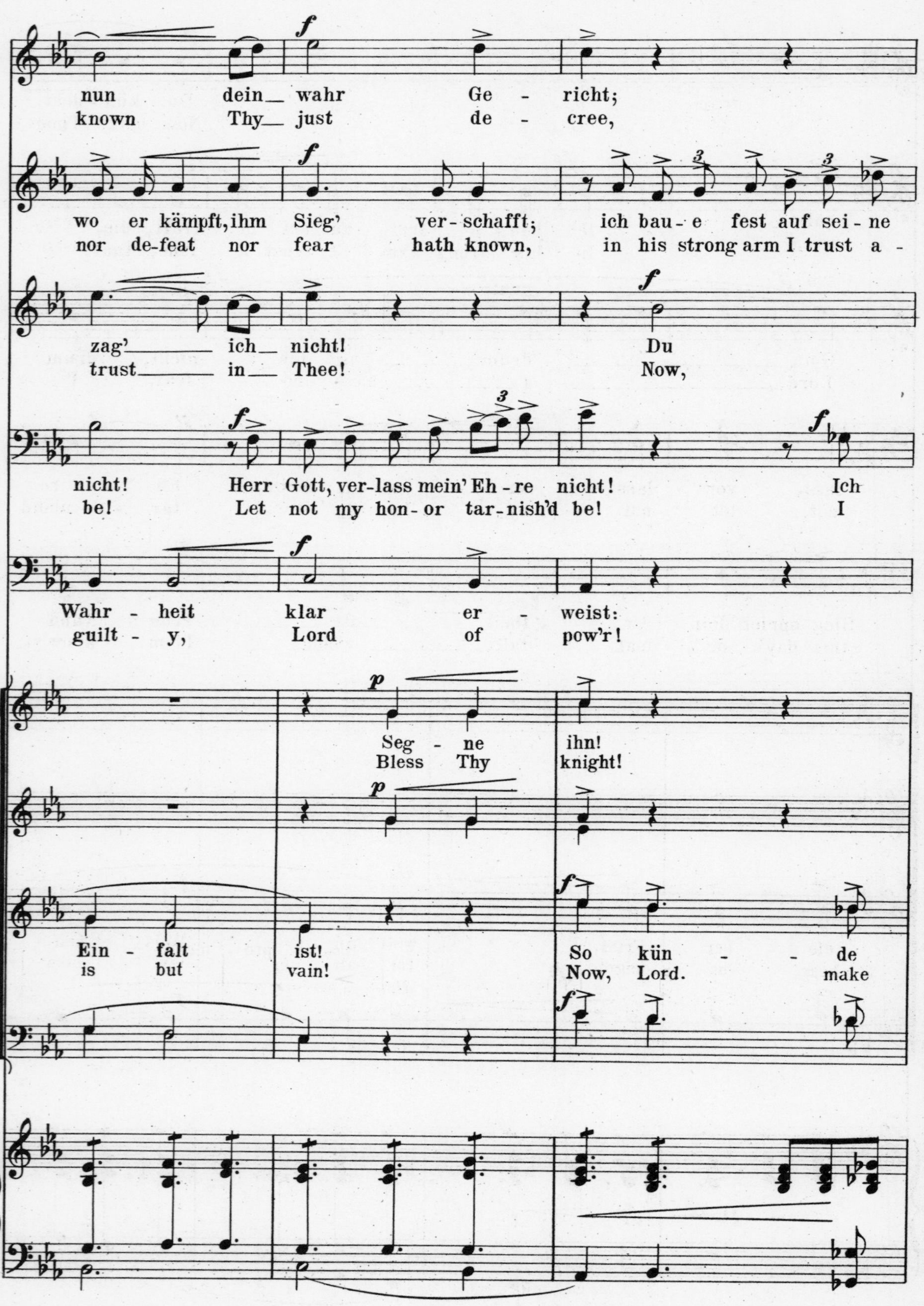
nun dein wahr Ge - richt;
known Thy just de - cree,
wo er kämpft, ihm Sieg' ver - schafft; ich bau - e fest auf sei - ne
nor de-feat nor fear hath known, in his strong arm I trust a -
zag' ich nicht! Du
trust in Thee! Now,
nicht! Herr Gott, ver-lass mein' Eh - re nicht! Ich
be! Let not my hon - or tar-nish'd be! I
Wahr - heit klar er - weist:
guilt - y, Lord of pow'r!
Seg - ne ihn!
Bless Thy knight!
Ein - falt ist! So kün - de
is but vain! Now, Lord, make

drum zag' ich nicht,
I have no fear,
Kraft, die, wo er kämpft, ihm Sieg ver-
lone, that nor de - feat nor fear hath
kün-dest nun dein wahr Ge - richt; mein Herr und
Lord, make known Thy just de - cree, oh Lord, make
geh' in Treu' vor dein Ge-richt; Herr Gott, ver -
here a - wait Thy just de-cree, Let not my
so kün-de nun dein wahr Ge-richt, Herr, mein
Now make Thou known Thy just de-cree, gra-cious
Seg - ne ihn!
Bless Thy knight!
nun dein wahr Ge - richt, du Herr und
known Thy just de - cree, pro - tect the

drum nun zag' ich nicht; mein
for I trust in Thee, my
cresc.
schafft; ich bau - e fest auf sei - ne
known, in his strong arm I trust a -
Gott, drum zag' ich nicht, mein
known Thy just de - cree, my
lass mein' Eh - re nicht! Herr Gott, ver-lass mein'
hon - or tar-nish'd be! Let not my hon - or
cresc.
Gott, so kün - de uns dein wahr Ge -
Lord, oh Lord, make known Thy just de -
poco cresc.
Herr, mein
gra - - cious
poco cresc.
più f
Gott, nun zög' - re nicht!
right, we trust in Thee!
più f
Str. arco.
poco cresc.

più f
Herr und Gott, drum zag' ich nicht, drum zag' ich nicht, mein
gra-cious Lord, I have no fear, I trust in Thee, I
ff
Kraft, ich bau - e fest auf sei - ne
lone, in his strong arm I trust a -
Herr und Gott, drum zag' ich nicht, mein Herr und Gott, drum
gra-cious Lord, I have no fear, I trust in Thee, I
Eh - re nicht! Herr Gott, ver - lass,
tar-nish'd be! Great Lord, let not
richt! Mein Herr und Gott, nun zög' - re
cree! Pro - tect the right, we trust in
Gott! Herr, mein Gott,
Lord! Gra-cious Lord!
Du Herr, mein Gott,
Pro - tect the right,
Wind sustain.
mf
cresc.

Herr, mein Herr, drum zag' ich nicht!
have no fear, I trust in Thee!
ff
Kraft, die, wo er kämpft, ihm Sieg verschafft!
lone, that nor defeat nor fear hath known!
zag' ich nicht, drum zag' ich nicht!
have no fear, I trust in Thee!
ff
ver - lass mein' Eh - re nicht!
my hon-or tar - nish'd be!
nicht, Herr, mein Gott, nun zög' - re nicht!
Thee, yea, we trust, we trust in Thee!
ff
mein Gott, seg - ne ihn!
oh bless Thy true knight!
ff
nun zög' - re nicht!
we trust in Thee!
8
Tutti.
Vl. & Tnr.
più f
ff
ff
ff

(In excitement all resume their places, the six seconds remain standing beside the spears of the enclosure, the other men form a wider circle round them; Elsa and her ladies in the foreground under the oak, beside the King. On a sign from the Herald, the Trumpeters blow the call to battle: Lohengrin and Frederick make their final preparations.)

Vl.
ff
Vivo.
ff
Ped.
ff
'Cello.
Ped.
(Here Lohengrin with a
ff Tutti.
Ped.
mighty stroke fells Frederick to the earth.)
(Frederick tries to raise himself, staggers a few steps backwards, then falls.)
Ped.

Lohengrin. (with the point of his sword upon Frederick's throat.) (releasing him.)

Durch Got - tes Sieg ist jetzt dein Le-ben mein: ich schenk' es dir! mögst du der Reu' es weih'n!

By Heav'n's be-hest to me was vic-t'ry lent; thy life I spare, May'st thou in peace re - pent!

ff *Str.* 3 3 3

Andante. Vivo. (All the men resume

SOPRANO & ALTO. *ff* Sieg! Hail!

TENOR. *ff* Sieg! Hail!

BASS. *ff*

Wind *p* Andante. *p* Vivo. *ff* *Tutti.* Ped.

their swords, and thrust them back in their scabbards. The seconds draw out the spears, and the King takes down his shield from the oak. All triumphantly rush to the centre and fill the ground where the fight took place. Elsa hastens to Lohengrin.)

Sieg!
Hail!
Sieg!
Hail!
Sieg!
Hail!
Sieg!
Hail!

The King. (also thrusting his sword in the scabbard)
Sieg!
Hail!
Heil!
Great
Heil
he
Heil!
Great
Heil
he
Elsa.
O
Oh
fänd' ich Ju - bel-wei-sen,
joy, oh joy, oh that my
The King.
Sieg!
Hail!
dir,
ro,
Held!
Hail!
dir,
ro,
Held!
Hail!
Ob. & Cl. with voice.
Wind.
dei-nem Ruh-me gleich, dich wür - dig zu prei - sen, an
tongue thy name could praise, the songs of the an - gels for

höchstem Lo - be reich! In dir muss ich ver - ge - hen, vor
thee I would up - raise! My lord here I con - fess thee, I'll
Fl.
fp
dir schwind' ich da - hin! Soll ich mich se - lig
live for thee a - lone! Wilt thou di - vine - ly
molto espressivo.
se - hen, nimm Al - les, Al - les, was ich
bless me, oh take me, take me for thine
Str.
cresc.
Trombs.
bin, nimm Al - - - - -
own, oh take
più cresc.

(She sinks upon Lohengrin's breast.)
- les, nimm Al - les, was ich bin!
me, oh take me for thine own!
The King.
Er - tö - ne,
Ye min - strels,
Chorus.
The Men.
TENORS.
Er - tö - ne,
In - tone a
BASSES.
Tutti.
er - tö - ne, Sie - ges - wei - se,
in - tone a lay of pleas - ure,
Sie - ges - wei - se, dem Hel - den
lay of pleas - ure, a loud, a
dem Hel - den
a loud, a
Str.

dem Hel - den laut zum Prei - se!
a loud, — tri - umph - ant meas - ure!

laut zum höch - sten — Prei - se! Ruhm dei - ner
loud, tri - umph - ant — meas - ure! Great be thy

laut zum Prei - se!
umph - ant meas - ure!

laut zum höch - sten Prei - se!
loud, tri - umph - ant meas - ure!

ff

Ruhm dei - ner Fahrt! Preis dei - nem Kom - men!
Great be thy fame, Blest hour that brought thee!

Fahrt! — Preis dei - nem Kom - men! Heil dei - ner
fame, — Blest hour that brought thee! Glo - rious thy

Ped. * Ped. *

Heil dei - ner Art, Schüt - zer der From - men!
Glo - rious thy name, base he that fought thee,

Art, — Schüt - zer der From - men! Ruhm dei - ner
name, — base he that fought thee, great be thy

Ped. * Ped. *

Ruhm dei - ner Fahrt! Heil dei - ner Art!
Great be thy fame! Glo - rious thy name!
(with growing enthusiasm.)
Fahrt! Heil dei - ner Art! Du hast ge-
fame, Glo - rious thy name, Thou cam'st to
f
ff
'Cello & Basses.
Du hast ge-wahrt das Recht der Frommen! Preis dei-ner
Thou cam'st to save when grief be-sought thee! Great be thy
wahrt das Recht der From - men! Preis dei-nem Kom - men,
save when grief be - sought thee! Great be thy fame! and
Preis dei-ner Fahrt, ge-
Great be thy fame! and
Ortrud (gazing darkly and fixedly at Lohengrin.)
Fahrt! Heil dei-ner Art! Wer ist's, der ihn ge-
fame! Blest be thy name! Who is't that thus hath
(With the utmost enthusiasm.)
Heil dei-ner Art! Dich nur be-sin-gen wir, dir
bless'd be thy name! All praise to thee is due, thy
segnet dei-ne Art!
bless-ed be thy name!
ff

The King.
Ortrud.
schla - gen? Preis dei-ner Fahrt! Durch den ich machtlos
doom'd us? Prais'd be thy name! Who brings my pow'r to
ff
schal-len un-sre- Lie - der! Nie kehrt ein Held gleich dir zu-
name shall live in- sto - ry! Ne'er did a knight so true ful -
ff
The King.
Lohengrin (raising Elsa from his breast.)
bin? Heil dei - ner Art! Den Sieg
naught? Great be thy fame! Heav'n lent
SOPRANO.
mf
Wo fänd' ich Ju-bel-wei-sen,
All hail, thou glo-rious he-ro,
ALTO.
mf
Du hast ge-wahrt das
Blest be the hour that
mf
die-sen Lan-den wie-der! Du hast ge-wahrt das
fil the land with glo-ry! Blest be the hour that
mf
das
that
Vl. & Tnr.
sempre f Wind sustain.

hab' ich er-strit-ten durch dei - ne Rein' al -
me strength to right thee, that truth might stand con -
sei-nem Ruh-me gleich, ihn wür - dig zu prei-sen, an
who thy name can praise? the songs of the an - gels for
Recht der From - men! Heil dei-nem Kom - men,
hith - er brought thee! Long live in glo - ry,
Recht der From - men! Heil dei - nem Kom - men,
hith - er brought thee! Long live in glo - ry, men, oh
lein; nun soll, was du ge-lit-ten, dir
fess'd, but now I will re-quite thee, for
höch - stem Lo-be reich, ihn wür - dig zu prei - sen, ihn
thee on high I'd raise, the songs of the an - gels are
Heil dei-nem Kom - men und Heil dei - ner Fahrt, Heil dei-nem
long live in glo - ry, oh prais'd be thy name, oh blest and
Heil sei dei-nem
Thou shalt live in
Heil dei - ner Fahrt! Heil sei dei-nem Kom-men, dei-nem
prais'd be thy name, Thou shalt live in sto-ry, ev-er
Heil dei-nem Kommen, dei-ner Fahrt!
bless-ed and glorious be thy name!
Heil dei-nem Kom-men, dei-ner
Long live in glo-ry, ev-er
più f

Elsa.

ff

O fänd' ich Ju - bel-wei - sen,
Oh joy, oh joy, oh that my

Ortrud.

ff

Wer ist's, der ihn ge -
Who is't that thus hath

Lohengrin.

reich ver - gol - ten sein, nun soll, was du ge -
all thy sor - row past. Yes, now I will re -

ff

Frederick.

ff

Weh', mich hat Gott ge -
Woe, Heav'n it - self hath

The King.

ff

Heil sei dei - ner
Hail, blest be the

würdig zu prei - sen, Heil!
wor - thy to praise thee, Hail!

Kom - men, dei - ner Fahrt! Heil! Heil!
glo - rious be thy name, Hail! Hail!

Kom - men, dei - ner Fahrt! Heil! Heil!
glo - rious be thy name, Hail! Hail!

Kom - men, dei - ner Fahrt! Heil! Heil!
glo - rious be thy name, Hail! Hail!

più f

Heil dei - ner Fahrt! Heil! Heil!
prais'd be thy name, Hail! Hail!

Fahrt, Heil dei - ner Fahrt! Heil!
glo - rious be thy name, Hail!

ff

dei-nem Ruh-me gleich, dich wür - dig zu prei - sen, an
tongue thy name could praise, the songs of the an - gels on
schla-gen, vor dem ich machtlos bin? Sollt' ich vor ihm ver-
doom'd us, who brings my pow'r to naught? Oh had the earth en-
lit - ten, dir reich ver-gol - ten sein,
quite thee for all thy sor - row past,
schla-gen, durch ihn, durch ihn ich sieg-los
doom'd me, and brought my trusted sword to
Fahrt, dei-nem Kom - men! Heil dei-ner
pow'r that hath brought thee! Blest be the
Heil! Heil!
Hail! Hail!
Heil der Fahrt! Heil! Heil!
Hail to thee! Hail! Hail!
Heil! Heil!
Hail! Hail!
Heil! Heil! Heil!
Hail! Hail! Hail!
Heil dei - ner Fahrt!
Blest be thy name!
Heil dei-nem Kom-men, dei-ner Fahrt! Ge-
For ev - er glo-rious be thy name! Oh

höch - stem Lo - be reich! Ach, soll ich mich se - lig
high for thee I'd raise! Wilt thou di - vine - ly
za - gen, wär' all' mein Hof - fen hin? Wär'
tomb'd us ere we to shame were brought! ere
was du ge - lit - ten, soll dir
I will re - quite thee, yea, for
bin; durch ihn, durch ihn sieg -
naught, 'tis heav'n that brought my
Fahrt, dei - nem Kom - men, dei - ner Fahrt! Heil dei - nem
hour that hath brought thee, val - iant knight! Hail, great in
dei - nem Kom - men!
live in glo - ry!
Heil dei - nem Kom - men, dei - ner Fahrt! Ge - seg - net dei - ne
For ev - er glo - rious be thy name! Oh glo - rious be thy
Heil dei - ner Fahrt! Ge - seg - net dei - ne
Blest be thy name! Oh glo - rious be thy
Heil dei - ner Fahrt! Heil dei - ner Fahrt! Ge - seg - net dei - ne
Blest be thy name! Blest be thy name! Oh glo - rious be thy
seg - net dein Kom - men, dei - ne Fahrt!
Bles - sed and glo - rious be thy name!

se - - hen, nimm Al - - les,
bless me, oh take me
all' mein Hof - fen hin?
we to shame were brought!
reich, ja reich ver -
all, for all thy
- los ich bin!
sword to naught!
Kom - men, dei - ner Fahrt! Er-tö -
glo - ry, great in fame! Ye min -
Er - tö - ne, Sie - ges -
In tone a lay of
Fahrt! Heil! Heil! Er tö - ne, Sie - ges -
name! All hail! In tone a lay of
Fahrt! Heil! Heil! Er tö - ne, Sie - ges -
name! All hail! In tone a lay of
Fahrt! Heil! Heil! Er tö - ne, Sie - ges -
name! All hail! In tone a lay of
Tutti.
Cymbals.
ff
Str.

was- ich bin!
for thine own!
ff (enraged)
Wer ist's, der ihn ge-
Who is't, who thus hath
gol- - - - ten sein!
sor- - - - row past!
- ne, Sie - ges - wei - se, dem Hel - den laut zum höch - sten
- strels, sing of pleas - ure, in - tone a loud, tri - umph - ant
wei - - - se, dem Hel - den laut zum höch - sten
pleas - - - ure, a loud, a loud, tri - umph - ant
wei- - - se, dem Hel - den laut zum
pleas - - - ure, a loud, tri - umph - ant
wei- - - se, dem Hel - den laut zum höchsten
pleas - - - ure, a loud, a loud, tri - umphant
wei- - - se, dem Hel - den laut zum höchsten
pleas - - - ure, a loud, a loud, tri - umphant

In dir muss ich ver- ge- hen!
Oh if my tongue could praise thee!
schla - gen? Vor dem ich macht - los bin?
doom'd me? Who brings my power to naught?
Den Sieg hab' ich er- run - gen
I will, I will re- quite thee,
Am Heil muss ich ver- za - gen! Mein'
Oh earth, hadst thou en- tomb'd me Ere
Prei - se! Ruhm dei - ner Fahrt!
meas - ure! Great be thy pow'r,
Prei - se! Ruhm dei - ner Fahrt, Preis dei - nem
meas - ure! Great be thy fame! long live in
Prei - se! Ruhm dei - ner Fahrt, Preis dei - nem
meas - ure! Great be thy fame! long live in
Prei - se! Ruhm dei - ner Fahrt, Preis dei - nem
meas - ure! Great be thy fame! long live in

Vor dir schwind' ich da-hin! Soll
All sor - - row now hath flown! Wilt
Wer ist's, vor dem ich macht - los bin?
Who is't, whobringsmy pow'r to naught?
durch dei - ne Rein' al - lein!
for all thy sor - row past!
Ruhm und Ehr' ist hin! Am Heil muss ich ver -
I to this was brought! Oh earth, hadst thou en -
Heil dei - ner Art! Ruhm dei - ner Fahrt! Heil dei - ner
Glo - rious thy name! Great be thy fame! Blest be thy
Kommen! Heil dei - ner Art, Schüt - zer der Frommen!
glo-ry! Great be thy fame, long live in glo - ry!
Kommen! Heil dei - ner Art, Schüt - zer der Frommen!
glo-ry! Great be thy fame, long live in glo - ry!
Kommen! Heil dei - ner Art, Schüt - zer der Frommen!
glo-ry! Great be thy fame, long live in glo - ry!

ich mich se - lig se - hen, nimm
thou di-vine - ly bless me, Oh
Sollt' ich vor ihm ver-za-gen?
Oh had the earth en-tomb'd us,
Nun soll, was du ge-
Heav'n lent me strength to
za - gen!
tomb'd me
Mein' Ruhm und
Ere I to
Art! Heil dei - ner Art! Heil!
name! Great be thy fame! Hail!
Preis dei - ner Fahrt! Heil dei - ner Art!
Blest be thy name! Great be thy fame!
Preis dei - ner Fahrt! Heil dei - ner Art!
Blest be thy name! Great be thy fame!
Preis dei - ner Fahrt! Heil dei - ner Art!
Blest be thy name! Great be thy fame!

Al - - - - - - les, nimm Al - - -
take me, oh take
Wär' all' mein Hof - fen hin? Sollt' ich vor
ere we to shame were brought! Oh had the
lit - ten, dir reich ver - gol - ten sein!
rightthee, that truth might stand con - fest,
Ehr' ist hin! Mein' Ruhm und Ehr,' mein' Ruhm und
this was brought, Ere I to this, ere I to
Heil! Heil dei - nem Kom - men! Heil dei - ner
Hail! Blest hour that brought thee! Great be thy
Dir tö - nen Sie - ges - wei - - sen! Heil
Blest be the hour that brought thee, Great
Dir tö - nen Sie - ges - wei - - sen! Heil
Blest be the hour that brought thee, Great
Dir tö - nen Sie - ges - wei - - - sen! Heil
Blest be the hour that brought thee, Great

les, Al - - les was ich bin!
me, take me for thine own,
ihm, vor ihm ver- za - gen, sollt' ich vor
earth, the earth en- tomb'd us, oh had the
Nun soll, was du ge- lit - ten, dir
But now I will re- quite thee, for
Ehr' ist hin! Mein' Ruhm und
this was brought! Ere I to
Fahrt! Heil dei- nem Kom - men! Heil dei- nem
fame, blest hour that brought thee, blest hour that
dei- ner Fahrt, dei - ner Art!
be thy fame ev - er - more,
dei- ner Fahrt, dei - ner Art!
be thy fame ev - er - more,
dei- ner Fahrt, dei - ner Art!
be thy fame ev - er - more,
Tpts., Tromb. & Tb.

Nimm Al - les, Al - - - - -
All for thine own,
ihm ver - za - - - gen? Wär'
earth en - tomb'd us, ere
reich ver - gol - ten sein, nun soll, was
all thy sor - row past, I will, I
Ehr' ist hin! Weh', mich hat
this was brought! Woe, Heav'n it -
Kom - men, dei - ner Fahrt! Heil dei - ner Fahrt, Heil
brought thee, val - iant knight: Great be thy fame, blest
Heil dei - ner Fahrt!
Glo - rious thy name!
Heil dei - ner Fahrt! Heil, Heil
Glo - rious thy name! Hail, Blest
Heil dei - ner Fahrt! Heil dei - ner Fahrt, Heil
Glo - rious thy name! Great be thy fame, blest
Heil dei - ner Fahrt! Heil dei - ner Fahrt, Heil
Glo - rious thy name! Great be thy fame, blest
ff
ff
ff

all' mein Hof - fen hin, wär' all' mein
we to shame were brought, ere we to
du ge - lit - ten, was du ge - lit - ten,
will re - quite thee, I will re - quite thee,
Gott ge - schla - gen, durch ihn ich
self hath doom'd me, and brought my
dei - nem Kom - men! Heil dei - ner Fahrt, Heil,
hour that brought thee, great be thy fame, hail,
Heil, Heil, Heil dei - ner
Hail, hail, Blest be thy
dei - nem Kom - men, dei - ner Fahrt, Heil,
hour that brought thee, hail to thee, all
dei - nem Kom - men, Heil dei - ner Fahrt, Heil,
hour that brought thee, all hail to thee, all
dei - nem Kom - men, Heil dei - ner Fahrt, Heil,
hour that brought thee, all hail to thee, all
8

-les, was ich bin, nimm Al - -
— oh for thine own, oh take
Hof - fen hin? Wär' all mein Hof - -
shame were brought, ere we to shame
was du ge-lit - ten, dir reich ver -
I will re-quite thee, for all thy
sieg - los bin! Am Heil muss ich ver-
sword to naught! Oh earth, had'st thou en-
Heil dei - nem Kom - men! Heil
hail to thy com - ing! Blest
Art! Heil dir, Heil dir, Heil dei -
name! all hail, all hail, All hail
Heil, Heil dir, Heil dir,
hail, all hail, all hail,
Heil, Heil dir, Heil dir, Heil dei -
hail, all hail, all hail, All hail
Heil, Heil dir, Heil dir, Heil dei -
hail, all hail, all hail, All hail
ff
8
Ped.
*

- les, was ich bin! Nimm es hin,
— me for thine own, I am thine,
- fen hin? Wär' es hin?
— were brought, Who is this?
gol - ten sein! Dir soll
sor - rows past, for all,
za - gen! Mein' Ruhm und Ehr'
tomb'd me, ere I to this,
— dei - ner Fahrt, Heil dir!
— be thy name, All hail!
- ner Art, Heil dir!
— to thee, all hail!
- ner Art, Heil dir!
— to thee, all hail!
- ner Art, Heil dir!
— to thee, all hail!
Tpts., Tromb.& Tb.
Vl., Tnr.& 'Cello.
ff
'Cello & Bass.

Al - les hin! O nimm Al - les
I am thine, take me for thine
Wär' es hin? Wär' all' Hof - fen
Who is this Brings my pow'r to
nun reich ver - gol - - - ten
for all thy sor - - - rows
ist da - hin! Mein' Ruhm und Ehr' ist da -
ere to this, ere I to this was
Preis dir, Heil dir, Heil dir, Heil dei - ner
all hail, all hail, all hail, blest be thy
SOPRANO & ALTO.
Preis dir, Heil dir, Heil dir, Heil dir, Heil
glo - ry, all hail, all hail, all hail, all
TENORS.
Preis dir, Heil dir, Heil dir, Heil dir, Heil
glo - ry, all hail, all hail, all hail, all
BASSES.

hin!
own!
hin!
naught?
sein!
past!
hin!
brought!
Fahrt!
name!
dir!
hail!
dir!
hail!
Tutti.
ff
(Frederick falls senseless at the feet of Ortrud. Youths raise Lohengrin upon his shield, and Elsa upon the shield of the King, upon which several have spread their mantles; thus both are borne away amid general rejoicing.)
(The curtain falls.)

End of the first Act.

Act II.

First Scene.

(On the stage behind the scenes.) *2 Flutes & Piccolo, 3 Oboes, 3 Clarinets in C, 2 Bassoons, 3 Horns in D, 3 Trombones, Kettle Drum in D, Cymbals.*

(In the Orchestra.) *3 Flutes, 2 Oboes, Corno inglese, 2 Clar.s in A. Bass Clar. in A, 3 Bss'ns, Horns in E & D, 3 Trumpets, 3 Trombones, Bass Tuba, Kettle Drums in F♯ & C♯, & Strings.*

(The curtain rises. Scene, the citadel of Antwerp; at the back the Palas (dwelling of Knights); in the foreground the Kemenate (dwelling of women); r.h. the Minster. It is night. Ortrud and Frederick, both in dark, servile garments, are seated on the steps of the Minster; Frederick is musing gloomily, Ortrud gazing fixedly at the windows of the Palas, which is brightly illuminated.)

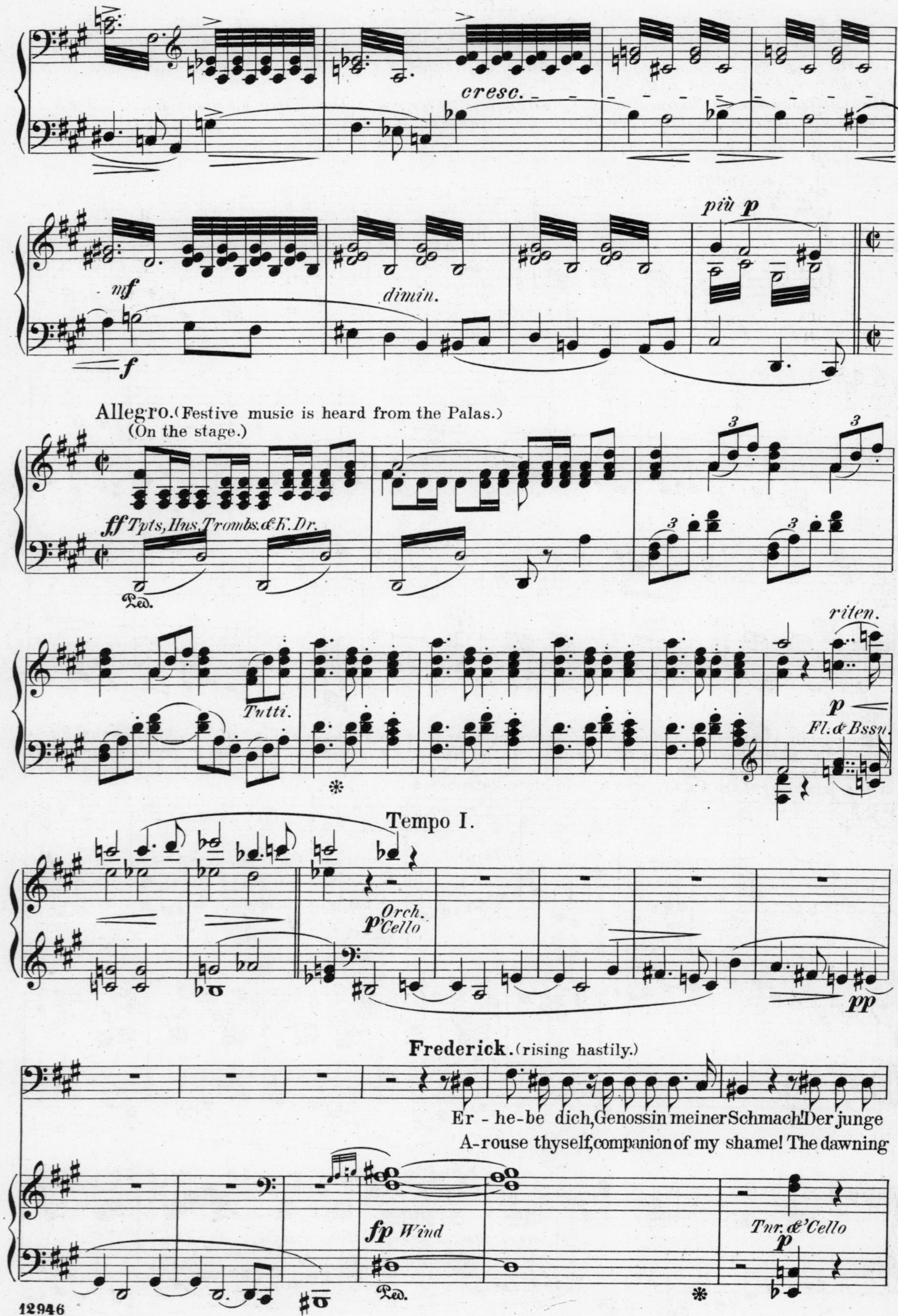
cresc.
mf
f
dimin.
più p
Allegro. (Festive music is heard from the Palas.)
(On the stage.)
ff Tpts, Hns, Trombs. & K. Dr.
Tutti.
riten.
p
Fl. & Bssn.
Tempo I.
Orch.
p Cello
pp
Frederick. (rising hastily.)
Er - he-be dich, Genossin meiner Schmach! Der junge
A-rouse thyself, companion of my shame! The dawning
fp Wind
Tnr. & Cello
p

Ortrud. (without altering her position.)
Tag darf hier uns nicht mehr sehn. Ich kann nicht fort: hie - her bin ich ge -
day we here may not a - wait. I can-not flee; some spell holds me en-
Cor. ingl.
pp
p Bass Cl.
pp Wind.
p
'Cello.
bannt. Aus die-sem Glanz des Fes-tes un-srer Fein - de lass sau-gen mich ein
chain'd. Yon fes - tive hall, where joy triumphant reign - eth, with - in my soul dis-
pp
p Wind.
furchtbar töd-lich Gift, das un-sre Schmach und ih-re Freu - den en - de!
tils the dead-ly bane that shall a - venge our cruel wrongs, and end them!
Str.
fp
f
fp
più p
pp
Frederick. (gloomily confronting Ortrud.)
Du fürch - ter-li-ches Weib! was bannt mich noch in dei-ne Nä-he?
What dark, mys-terious spell binds me to thee, un-ho-ly wo-man!
poco cresc.
(with growing vehemence.)
Warum lass ich dich nicht al-lein, und flie-he fort, da -
Ah, why can I from thee not fly, where I might find some
accel.
fp
fp

(with anguish)
riten.
hin, da - hin, wo mein Ge - wis - sen Ru - he wie - der
rest, some peace, where my dis - tract - ed soul could be at
Wind
f riten.
fp
p
(in a paroxysm of grief and rage.)
Vivo.
fänd'! Durch dich musst' ich ver-
rest! 'Tis thou whose spells have
accelerando
Str.
molto cresc.
Wind sustain
lie - - ren mein' Ehr', all' mei - nen
cost me My hon - or and my
Ruhm; nie soll mich Lob mehr
fame, Thou hast my knight - hood
zie - ren, Schmach ist mein Hel - den - thum! Die
lost me, Thou'st led me on to shame! My

Acht ist mir ge - spro - chen, zer -
sword lies stain'd and brok - en, My
trüm - mert liegt mein Schwert, mein Wap - pen ward zer -
shield is cast to earth, My name with curs - es
bro - chen, ver - flucht mein Va - ter - herd!
spoken, I'm 'reft of home and hearth!
Wo - hin ich nun mich wen - de, ge -
Wher - e'er for rest I turn me, Ab -
flohn, ge - fehmt bin ich; dass ihn mein Blick nicht
horr'd from me they fly; The vil - est wretch may
mf
ff
p
f
dim.

schän - de, flieht selbst der Räu - ber mich. Durch dich, durch
spurn — me, None is so vile as I! 'Tis thou, 'tis
ff
ff
dim.
p
K.Dr.
Tur.& Cello
dich musst' ich ver-lie-ren mein' Ehr', all' meinen Ruhm;
thou, thou who hast cost me My hon-or and my fame,
Vl.
f
p
nie soll mich Lob mehr zie-ren, Schmach — ist mein Hel-den-thum! Die
Thou hast my knighthood lost me, Thou'st — led me on to shame! My
cresc.
Acht — ist mir ge-spro-chen, zer-trüm - mert liegt mein
sword — lies stain'd and brok-en, My shield — is cast to
ff
Tutti
p
ff
p
Schwert, mein Wap - pen ward zer-bro-chen, ver-
earth, My name — with curs-es spok-en, I'm
ff
p

flucht mein Va-ter-herd!
'reft of home and hearth!
ff
p
f
più f
Hns. & Bssn.
Str.
più p
pp
(almost weeping.)
O, hätt' ich Tod er-ko-ren, da ich so e-lend bin!
Oh had but death o'er-ta'en me I had my hon-or sav'd!
(with utter desperation.)
Mein Ehr', mein Ehr' hab' ich ver-
But thus, as mis-creant to ar-
Hns. & Bssn. sustain.
molto cresc.
più f
ff Tutti mf
lo-ren, mein' Ehr', mein' Ehr' ist hin, mein' Ehr', mein' Ehr' ist hin!
raign me, My sword, My name dis-grac'd, my sword, my name dis-grac'd!
cresc.
(He throws himself on the ground, overwhelmed with anguish.)

(Music sounds in the Palas.)
ff Tpts.& Trombs.(on the stage.)
Ped.
Ortrud. (without quitting her first position while Frederick rises.)
Was macht dich in so wil-der Kla-ge doch ver-
Why dost thou thus in i-dle grief thy heart con-
Slower.
Wind.
p Orch.
Ped.
Frederick.
(with a violent gesture.)
geh'n? Dass mir die Waffe selbst geraubt, mit der ich dich er-schlüg'!
sume? Wom-an, be-cause I have no sword with which to strike thee dead!
Str.
f
Ped.
Ortrud.(with quiet scorn)
Friedreicher Graf von
Well art thou nam'd the
Wind.
p
Ped.
Tel-ra-mund! wes-halb miss-traust du mir?
peaceful one! why dost thou doubt in me?
Frederick.
Du fragst? War's nicht dein Zeugniss, deine Kunde, die mich be-
Why doubt? Was't not thy showing, thy beguiling that led me
Ped.

strickt, die Rei-ne zu ver-kla-gen?
on t'ac-cuse yon spotless maiden?
Str.
Die du im dü-stern Wald zu Haus,
When in thy dis-mal for-est home,
logst du mir nicht, von dei-nem wil-den Schlos-se aus die
didst thou not say, that from its ru-in'd tow'r thou saw'st how
Un-that habest du ver-ü-ben sehn?
El-sa did the foul and murd'rous deed?
mit eig-nem Aug', wie El-sa selbst den Bruder im
Then didst thou lie, or in the castle-moat did she
f
p Wind sustain
Wei-her dort er-tränkt?
not her brother drown?
Um-strick-test du mein stol-zes Herz durch die Weis-sa-gung
To lure my heart with wi-ly spells thou didst false-ly pre-
f
fp
nicht, bald wür-de Rad-bod's al-ter Für-sten-stamm von neu-em grü-nen und
dict Rad-bod's re-nown'd and an-cient house ere long should rise a-new and give
p Wood.
più p
pp Trombs. added.

herrschen in Bra-bant? Be-wogst du so mich nicht, von El-sa's Hand, der Rei-nen, ab-zu-
princes to Bra-bant? 'Twas thus, en-tic'd by thee, that El-sa's Hand, the peerless, I re-
Str.
fp
Ortrud. (with suppressed rage.)
steh'n, und dich zum Weib zu nehmen, weil du Radbod's letzter Spross! Ha, wie töd-lich du mich kränkst!
nounc'd, and took thee for my consort, as the last of Radbod's race? Oh, how dead-ly is his scorn!
Wind.
Frederick. (with great animation.)
Allegro.
(aloud.)
Dies Al-les, ja, ich sagt' und zeugt' es dir! Und machtest mich, dess' Na-me hoch-ge-
I grant it, yea, all this I prov'd to thee! Thou madest me, whose name was well re-
Str. pizz.
ehrt, dess' Le-ben al-ler höchsten Tugend Preis, zu dei-ner Lü-ge
nown'd, Whose knighthood was untainted by a flaw, of ly-ing arts a
Wind
Frederick.
Ortrud. (defiantly.)
schändlichem Ge-nos-sen? Wer log? Du! Hat nicht durch sein Gericht Gott
dupe and an accomplice! Who lied? Thou! Was not the judgment clear? Heav'n
Str.
Wind.
dim.
Trombs.
Str.

rather slower.
Vivo.
Ortrud. (with terrible scorn.)
Frederick.
_mich da-für ge - schla-gen?
_hath declar'd a - gainst me!
Gott?
Heav'n?
Ent-
Oh
Vivo.
Tutti.
Str.
setz-lich! Wie tönt aus dei - nem Mun - de furcht-bar der Na - me!
hor-ror! That wont-ed word of hope, on thy lips how dreadful!
Ortrud.
Ha,
Ha,
Frederick
Ortrud.
nennst du dei - ne Feigheit Gott?
is thy hope the coward's Heav'n?
Ortrud!
Ortrud!
Willst du mir droh'n? mir, einem Weibe,
What means thy threat? wouldst thou assail thy
Tutti.
Str.
poco cresc.
droh'n? O Fei - ger! hättest du so grimmig ihm gedroht, der jetzt dich in das
wife? Oh cra - ven! If thou hadst but threaten'd him like this, who dooms us to this
E - lend schickt, wohl hät-test Sieg für Schan - de du er-
bit - ter woe well hadst thou won, and glo - rious were thy

p lento.
kauft! Ha, wer ihm zu ent-geg-nen wüsst', der fänd' ihn schwächer als ein Kind!
name! Ah, if thou wouldst but hearken now, there is a spell can lay him low!
lento.
fp
Trombs.&Tb.
pp
p
Frederick.
Je schwächer er, des-to gewalt'ger kämpfte Got-tes Kraft!
No spell a-vails, all heav'nly pow-ers on his side are rang'd!
Str. poco più moderato
pp
poco cresc.
f
p
Ortrud.
ff
Got-tes Kraft? Ha, ha! Gieb mir die Macht, und si-cher zeig' ich dir, welch'
Heav'n-ly pow'rs? Ha, ha! Mark but my word, and I will show to thee how
ff Wind.
ff
schwa-cher Gott es ist, der ihn be-schützt.
weak those heav'n-ly pow'rs, that fight for him.
Moderato.
Str.
pizz.
Wind.
f
p
pp
K. dr.
Frederick. (shuddering, in a low, trembling voice.)
p
pp
Du wil-de Se-he-rin! wie willst du doch ge-heimniss-voll den Geist mir neu be-
Thou god-less prophetess! and dost thou think thy sub-tle spells a-gain to weave a-
Cor. ingl.

Ortrud. (pointing to the Palas, where the lights are now extinguished.)

rü - cken? Die Schwelger streck-ten sich zur üpp'- - gen Ruh;
round me? Of feast-ing wea - ry, they are slum - b'ring now.

setz' dich zur Sei - te mir! Die Stund' ist da, wo dir mein Se - her-au - ge
Come, seat thee here by me! The hour is nigh when yonder stars re-veal their

(Frederick draws nearer to Ortrud, and bends his ear attentively to her words.)

leuch-ten soll!
lore to me!

Str. con Sord. *pp*

B. Cl. *p*

Weisst du, wer die-ser
Know'st thou who is yon

Held, den hier ein Schwan ge - zo - gen an das Land?
knight, who by a swan was guided to our land?

p

Frederick. Nein!
No!

Ortrud. Was gäbst du
Shall I re-

p Cor. ingl. & Bssn.

doch, es zu er-fah-ren, wenn ich dir sag', ist er ge - zwungen zu nen - nen,
veal to thee his se-cret? Mark what I say, if aught com-pel him to an - swer

B. Cl. *p*

wie sein Nam' und Art, all sei - ne Macht zu En-de ist, die müh-voll ihm ein
what his race and name, his vaunted pow'r is par-a-lyz'd, the spell that lends him
Wind.
Str.
Frederick.
Ortrud.
Zau - ber leiht? Ha! Dann be - griff' ich sein Ver-bot! Nun hör'!
strength, dis-solv'd. Ha, was't for that, then, he for-bade_For that!
Ob.&Cl.
dim.
Str.
più p
Cor. ingl. & B. Cl.
Nie-mand hier hat Ge - walt, ihm das Ge - heim-niss zu ent-reis-sen, als
No one here hath the pow'r from him to draw the fa-tal se-cret, but
Frederick.
die, der er so streng ver-bot, die Fra-ge je an ihn zu thun. So gält' es,
she, whom he so stern - ly bade that she the question ne'er should ask. To ask him,
Ortrud.
Elsa zu ver-lei-ten, dass sie die Frag' ihm nicht er-liess'? Ha, wie begreifst du schnell und
Elsa must be tempted, 'tis she a - lone can break the spell! Ha, thou art swift to un - der-

Frederick.
Ortrud.
wohl! Doch wie soll das ge - lin - gen? Hör'! Vor Al - lem gilt's, von
stand! How can she be per - suad - ed? Mark, a - bove aught else, from
Ob.
Fl.
p
hin - nen nicht zu flieh'n; drum schär - fe dei - nen Witz! Ge - rech - ten Argwohn ihr zu
hence we must not fly; then nerve thee to the task: Her just suspi - cion we must
cresc.
(with great decision.)
più moto.
wecken, tritt vor, klag' ihn des Zau - bers an, mit dem er das Gericht ge -
kindle; go forth, say that by sor - ce - ry, he triumph'd o'er a right - eous
Vl.
fp
Tnr. & 'Cello.
Frederick. (gradually lashed into a furious passion.)
accelerando.
täuscht! Ha! Trug, und Zau - - bers
cause! Ha! yea, 'twas sor - ce -
cresc.
più f
Ortrud.
Frederick.
Vivo.
f
Ortrud.
List! Missglückt's, so bleibt ein Mit - tel der Ge - walt! Gewalt! Um -
ry! At worst, if that should fail, she must be forc'd! Be forc'd? Not
Wind.
Str. senza sord.
ff
p
ff Vivo. ff

(a little slower.)
sonst nicht bin ich in ge - heim-sten Künsten tief er - fah-ren; drum ach-te
all in vain the se-cret lore of old to me's fa - mil-iar; store in thy
p
wohl, was ich dir sa - ge! Jed' We - sen, das durch Zau - ber stark,
mind what now I tell thee! Strength that is lent by mag - ic art,
più p
pp
B.Cl.
wird ihm des Leibes kleinstes Glied ent-ris - sen nur, muss sich als - bald ohn - mäch-tig
fails, if of him bewitch'd one drop of blood be shed, his na - tive help-less - ness and
(with animation.)
zei - gen, wie es ist! O hättest du im Kampf nur ei - nen
frail - ty then is shown. Oh, if thou in the com - bat hadst but
Frederick. (impetuously.)
Animato.
Ha, sprächst du wahr!
Oh, were that true!
pp
f
p
Fin-ger ihm, ja, ei-nes Fin-gers Glied entschlagen, der Held, er war in deiner
wounded him, yea, if thou hadst but maim'd his fin-ger, the dough - ty knight were in thy
cresc.
f

Allegro con moto agitato.
Frederick.
Macht! Ent-setz- -lich! Ha, was lässest du mich
pow'r! Oh mad- -ness! Ha, that I too late must
Tutti.
hö - ren? Durch Gott ge-schla - gen wähnt ich mich:
learn it! 'Twas Heav'n I thought de-feat-ed me!
più f
ff trem.
(with terrible bitterness.)
Nun liess durch Trug sich das Ge-richt be-
I was his dupe, the judgment naught but
f Wind.
thö - ren, durch Zau- - bers List ver-lor mein'
false-hood, by sor- - c'rer's art I have mine
ff Tutti.
fp

Eh- - -re ich! Doch mei-ne
hon- - -or lost! Can I a-
Vl.
ff
p Wind sustain.
pp
Schan - de könnt' ich rä-chen, be-zeu- -gen könnt' ich mei-ne
venge the vile de-lu-sion, Re-gain my knighthood and my
f
p
Treu'? Des Buh - len Trug ich könnt' ihn bre-chen,
sword? And bring up-on those two con-fu-sion,
f
p
cresc.
und mei- -ne Ehr' gewönn' ich neu?
Thus were my hon- - -or back re-stor'd?
f
mf
Ped.

O Weib, das in der Nacht ich vor mir seh' be-
Oh thou, who dost the pow'rs of darkness know, If
molto cresc.
ff
p
trügst du jetzt mich noch, dann weh' dir!
thou speak false-ly now, woe on thee!
ff
Weh'!
woe!
Ortrud.
rallentando poco a poco.
Ha, wie du ra-sest! Ru-hig und be-
Nay, thou art rav-ing. Tem-per wrath with
ff dim.
Fl., Cor. ingl. & Cl.
p
son-nen! So lehr' ich dich der Ra-che sü-sse Wonnen!
meas-ure! And I will teach thee ven-geance, God-like pleasure!
Moderato.
Str.
p Wind.
pp
B.Cl. & Bssn.
(Frederick slowly seats himself beside Ortrud.)
molto cresc.
ff
dim.
Trombs. & Tb.

Ortrud.
Der Ra - che Werk sei nun be-schwo - ren aus
For dread re - venge here I im - plore ye, Oh
Frederick.
Der Ra - che Werk sei nun be-schwo - ren aus
For dread re - venge here I im - plore ye, Oh
più p
pp
cresc.
f Tutti.
dim.
mei - nes Bu - sens wil - der Nacht!
Pow'rs that rule our earth - ly lot,
Die ihr in
Ye, who now
pp Str.
pp
sü - ssem Schlaf ver-lo - ren, wisst, dass für euch das
dream that joy's be-fore ye, Know, that our ven - geance
f
diminuendo.

Un - heil wacht! Die ihr in
slum - bers not! Ye, who now

Un - heil wacht! Die ihr in
slum - bers not! Ye, who now

pp *fp*

sü - ssem Schlaf ver - lo - ren,
dream that joy's be - fore ye,

sü - ssem Schlaf ver - lo - ren,
dream that joy's be - fore ye,

dim.

wisst, dass für euch das Un - heil wacht!
Know, that our ven - geance slum - bers not!

wisst, dass für euch das Un - heil wacht!
Know, that our ven - geance slum - bers not!

più p *pp* *Trombs.* *Ped.*

(Here the door of the Kemenate, that leads on to the balcony, opens.)

B.Cl. *Trombs.* *Wood.* *

Second Scene.

Same score (Cl.& B.Cl.in B., Horns in F & C.)

(Elsa, in a white robe, appears on the balcony; she steps forward to the parapet and leans her head on her hand; Frederick and Ortrud, opposite to her, sit on the steps of the Minster.)

wahrt.
be.
Ortrud.
Zu trocknen mei-ne
Wher-e'er thy pinion
Der Stun-de soll sie fluchen, in der sie jetzt mein Blick ge-wahrt!
Be near, ye pow'rs of darkness, may she for ev-er rue this hour!
Ob.
espress.
p
poco rallent.
mf
Zäh-ren hab' ich euch oft ge-müht; wollt Küh-lung nun ge-wäh-ren der
rush-eth, The mourner's tears are dried, My cheek that burns and flusheth With
pp
poco rallent.
Frederick.
Wang', in Lieb er-glüht!
love, oh cool and hide!
Wa-rum?
But why?
Ortrud.
Hinweg! Ent-fern' ein Klei-nes dich von hier!
A-way! thou must a-while from hence de-part!
mf
più p
p espress.
Elsa.
Wollt Küh-lung nun ge-währen
My cheek that burns and flusheth
(Frederick disappears at the back.)
Sie ist für mich, ihr Held ge-hö-re dir!
Leave her to me, her knight shall be for thee!
Cl.

der Wang', in Lie - be, in Lie - be, in Lieb' er -
With love oh cool thou, oh cool thou, oh cool and
Fl.
pp
Wood.
glüht! In Lie - be!
hide! Oh cool thou!
(calls, in a plaintive voice.)
El - sa!
El - sa!
Fl.
Ob. & Hns.
Wer ruft? Wie schau - er - lich und kla - gend er -
Who calls? How drea - ri - ly and strange - ly my
Fl.
Ortrud.
tönt mein Na - me durch die Nacht?
name resoundeth thro' the night!
El - sa! Ist mei - ne Stimme dir so
El - sa! Hast thou for - gotten e'en my
Hn. & Fl.
Ob.
fremd? Willst du die Ar - me ganz ver - läug - nen, die du in's
voice? Wilt thou dis - own me in my sor - row, who am by
Fl. & Ob.
Ob.

Elsa.

fernste Elend schickst? Ortrud! bist du's? Was machst du hier, unglücklich Weib?
thee of all be - reft? Ortrud! 'tis thou? What dost thou here, woman un-blest?

Cor. ingl. *add Cl.*

Ortrud. **Moderato.**

"Unglücklich Weib!" wohl hast du Recht, so mich zu nennen! In fer - ner Einsamkeit des
"Woman unblest!" Yea, thou hast cause, unblest to call me! I dwelt in sol - itude pro -

Str. pizz. *Cor. ingl. & B. Cl.* *Wind.*

Wal - des, wo still und friedsam ich ge - lebt, — was that ich dir? was that ich
tect - ed, my home the deep and silent wood, I harm'd thee not, I harm'd thee

Str. *'Cello.*

dir? Freud - los, das Unglück nur beweinend, das lang' be - lastet meinen
not. Joy - less I mourn'd the ev - il fortune that long hath rested on my

Cor. ingl. & B. Cl. *Wind.*

Stamm, — was that ich dir? was that ich dir? **Elsa.** Um
race, I harm'd thee not! I harm'd thee not! Ah

Str. *Ob.* *'Cello.*

Gott, was kla-gest du mich an? War ich es, die dir Leid ge-
why, why speak to me of this? Thy sorrow was not caus'd by
Cl.
Ob.& Fl.
Fl. & Cl.
cresc.
Ortrud.
bracht? Wie könn - test du für - wahr mir nei - den das
me! 'Twere strange in-deed if thou didst en - vy my
Vl.
Cor. ing.
B. Cl. Fl., Cl. & Bssn.
f
p
Str. sustain.
Elsa.
Glück, dass mich zum Weib erwählt der Mann, den du so gern verschmäht? All-
lot, to be the wife of him whom scorn-ful-ly thy heart disdain'd. Ye
Ob.& Fl.
p
mf
p
Wind.
Ortrud.
güt' - ger Gott! Was soll mir das? Musst' ihn unsel'ger Wahn bethören,
guar - dian saints! why this to me? The vic - tim of a wild delusion,
Vl.
Wood.
mf
dim.
p
cresc.
fp
Str.
Ped.
*
dich Rei - ne ei-ner Schuld zu zeih'n, - von Reu' ist nun sein Herz zer-rissen, zu
he dared to cast a doubt on thee, since then he by remorse is riv-en, the
p
cresc.
fp

Elsa.
Ortrud.
Un poco più lento.
grimmer Buss' ist er ver-dammt. Gerech-ter Gott! O du bist
ban is spok-en o'er his head. Have mer-cy, Heav'n! Thou can'st be
Vl.
mf
f Wind.
glücklich! Nach kur-zem, unschuld-süssem Leiden, siehst lächeln du das Le-ben
hap-py! Thy brief and guileless morn of promise pre-par'd thee for a ra-diant
dimin.
p Tnr. & 'Cello divided.
nur; von mir darfst se-lig du dich scheiden, mich schickst du auf des To-des
noon; De-part from my un-ho-ly presence, from thee I may not crave a
p
pp
Spur, dass meines Jammers trü-ber Schein nie kehr' in dei-ne Fes-te
boon, I will not haunt thy fu-ture bright, Nor darken thy undimm'd de-
Vl.
cresc.
dim.
p Cl. & Bssn.
più p
D. Bass.
con moto.
Elsa (deeply moved.)
ein! Wie schlecht ich deine Gü-te prie-se, All-mächt'-
light! So blest I am, oh bounteous Heav-en, So great
cresc.
Str.

ger, der mich so be-
the boon I owe to
Wind sustain.
glückt, wenn ich das Un-glück von mir stie-sse, das sich im
thee, Ne'er from my side be sor-row driv-en, When in the
più p
Stau-be vor mir bückt! O nim-mer! Or-trud,
dust it sues to me! No nev-er! Or-trud,
cresc.
har-re mein! Ich sel-ber lass' dich zu mir ein!
wait thou there! Ere long a-gain I shall be near!
Molto Allegro.
Wind.
Str.
(She hastens back into the Kemenate; Ortrud springs from her seat on the Minster steps in wild exultation.)
Ortrud.
Ent-
Ye
Wind.
Trombs., B. Tb. & D. Bass.

weih - - te Göt - ter!
Gods ___ for - sak - en!

ffp Tutti. cresc.

Helft jetzt mei - ner Ra - che! Be -
grant, grant me your ven - geance! De -

Ob., Hns.& Bssn.
f cresc.

straft ___ die Schmach, ___ die
clare ___ your pow'r, ___ be

ff fp fp

hier euch an - ge - than! ___
nigh in this dread hour! ___

ff fp fp

Stärkt mich im Dienst eu - rer heil' - gen
Strike them with death who pro - fane your

pp f

Sa - che! Ver - nich - tet der Ab - trünn'- gen
al - tars! And strength - en my soul to a -
schnö - den Wahn!
venge your wrongs!
Tutti Wind.
Wo -
O -
molto cresc.
- dan!
- din!
Dich Star - ken ru - fe ich!
Thou strong and mighty one!
Tutti Wind.
Str.
Frei - a!
Frey - a!
Er - hab' - ne, hö - re mich!
Oh Queen, bend down to me!
Str.
Seg - net mir Trug und Heu - che - lei, dass
Pros - per my cause with dead - ly guile, Im -

glück - lich mei - ne Ra - - che
mor - tals, on my ven - - geance
Fl. Ob. & Clar.
cresc.
ff
sei!
smile!
Tutti.
Elsa (still outside.)
(Elsa, with two maids bearing lights, enters by the lower door.)
Or - trud! wo bist du?
Or - trud! where art thou?
Fl.
p Str.
p Wind.
Ortrud (humbly prostrating herself before Elsa.)
Hier, zu dei-nen Fü-ssen!
Here, be-fore thee kneel-ing!
f Str.
Elsa (starting back in alarm at the sight of Ortrud.)
Hilf Gott! So muss ich dich er - blicken, die ich in
Oh Heav'n! How sore - ly art thou stricken, Whom I in
f
p
f

Stolz und Pracht nur sah! Es will das Her-
pride and splen-dor saw! My heart's com-pas-
dim.
-ze mir er-sticken, seh' ich so nie-drig dich mir
-sion it doth quicken, Heav'n's dark de-cree I mark with
dim.
più
(Not too fast.)
nah! Steh' auf! O, spa-re mir dein Bit-ten!
awe! A-rise! oh do not thus en-treat me!
Wind.
Trug'st du mir Hass, ver-zieh ich dir; was du schon jetzt durch
Wert thou my foe, I par-don thee; And if through me thy
Str.
mich ge-lit-ten, das, bit-te ich, ver-zeih' auch mir, das, bit-te
heart hath sor-row'd, I hum-bly ask thou par-don me, I hum-bly
Wind.
Str.

Ortrud.
ich, ver- zeih' auch mir!
ask thou par - don me!
O ha - be Dank für so viel
My grateful thanks for all thy
Tnr.
Fl.
p Wind.
più p
p
Tnr. & Cello divided.
Elsa.
Gü - te! Der mor - gen nun mein Gat - te
good - ness! Of him whom I shall wed at
Vl.
più p
pp
Wind.
heisst, an - fleh' ich sein
morn, grace I'll crave for
Tnr. with voice.
Tnr. & Cello divided.
lieb - reich Ge - mü - the, dass Fried - rich auch er
thee and thy hus - band, a boon to me he'll
Wind.
Ortrud.
Gnad' er - weist. Du fes - selst
not re - fuse. Oh, hold my
mf
dim.

Elsa (with rising pleasurable emotion.)
mich in Dan - kes Ban - den! In Früh'n lass mich be - reit dich seh'n! Ge - schmückt mit präch - ti - gen Ge - wan - den sollst du mit mir zum Mün - ster geh'n:
heart in grate - ful bon - dage! By morn - ing's dawn be thou pre - par'd; at - tire thy - self in roy - al rai - ment, with me be - fore the al - tar go!
pp
dim.
p Wind.
Vl.
Wind.
Dort har - re ich des Hel - den mein, vor Gott sein Eh' - - ge - mahl zu
Then I shall meet my he - ro guide, in face of Heav'n to be his
Ob.
dim.
p Wind.
(with joyous pride.)
Str.
pp
cresc.

ff
slowly.
(rapturously.)
pp
sein, vor Gott sein Eh' - ge-mahl zu sein! Sein
bride, in face of Heav'n, to be his bride! His
Fl.
poco allarg.
f
p
p poco rit.
Wind.
Tur.
Eh' - ge - mahl!
bride to be!
Fl. & Clar.
Str.
pp
ff
Wind sustain.
Ortrud.
Wie kann ich sol - che Huld dir
How can I e'er for this re-
Tur.
p
dim.
Trombs. sustain.
Vl. & Basses pizz.
loh - nen, da macht - los ich und
quite thee, Since I hence - forth am
e - lend bin? Soll ich in
poor and lone? Though as thy
Vl. divided.
p
'Cello.

Gna - den bei dir woh - nen, stets blei - be
friend thou dost in - vite me, I must my -
poco rall. (drawing nearer to Elsa.)
ich dir Bett - le - rin! Nur
self thy vas - sal own! One
più p
un poco più lento.
ei - ne Kraft ist mir ge - ge - ben, sie
gift a - lone the gods have lent me, (None
pp Wood.
p
raub - te mir kein Macht - ge - bot; durch sie viel-leicht
si - lence to me hath or - dain'd), With that, per-chance,
pp
Str. con. Sord. Wood sustain.
schütz' ich dein Le - ben, be-wahr' es vor der Reu - e
I may pre - vent thee From trea - son, and thy life's at -

Elsa (artlessly and kindly.) Ortrud (vehemently.)
(moderating herself.)
Noth! Wie meinst du? Wohl dass ich dich war - - ne, zu blind nicht dei-nem Glück zu
taint! What say'st thou? As thy friend I warn thee, Lest thou in love too blind-ly
cresc.
Wind.
Bssn.
Più lento.
traun; dass nicht ein Un-heil dich um- - gar-ne, lass mich für dich zur Zukunft
trust; Lest cru-el for-tune change and spurn thee, For its de-crees are oft un-
Strs.
Elsa (shuddering inwardly.) Adagio. Ortrud (with great mystery.)
schaun. Welch' Un-heil? Könn-test du er - fas-sen, wie des-sen
just. What for-tune? May he nev-er leave thee, Who was by
Adagio.
Cor. ingl.
Wind.
B. Cl.
più p
Cello.
Art so wun-der-sam, der nie dich mö - ge so ver - las-sen, wie er durch
mag - ic hith - er brought, And may the glam - or ne'er de - ceive thee That in thy
(turns again to Ortrud full of compassion.)
(Elsa turns away, seized with secret dread.)
Più vivo.
Moderato. Elsa (Freely declaimed.)
Zau-ber zu dir kam! Du
soul his words have wrought! Oh
Str.
Wind.
Str.
12946

rit.
Aermste kannst wohl nie er-mes-sen, wie zwei-fel-los mein Her-ze liebt!
that thy heart could know the treas-ure Of love that knows not fear— or doubt!
pp colla parte.
Du hast wohl nie das Glück— be-ses-sen, das sich uns nur durch Glau-be
No child of earth that bliss— can measure, Who doth not dwell in faith de-
mf
p
più p
Wind.
più p
Moderato, a tempo. (kindly.)
giebt? Kehr' bei mir ein! Lass' mich dich leh-ren, wie
vout. Rest thee with me! Oh let me teach thee How
Ob.
p
Str.
p
süss die Won-ne rein-ster Treu'! Lass— zu dem Glau-ben
trust doth hal-low joy— and love! Turn— to our faith, I
Ob.
p
p

rallentando poco a poco.

dich be-keh-ren: es giebt ein Glück, es giebt ein Glück, das oh-ne
do be-seech thee, Our faith di-vine, our faith di-vine, for God is

Wind.

Molto tranquillo, ma non lento.

Reu'! Lass mich dich leh-ren, wie
love! O let me teach thee, how

Ortrud (aside.)

Ha! Die-ser Stolz, er soll mich leh-ren, wie ich be-käm-pfe ih-re
Oh! pride of heart, I yet will teach thee, That an il-lu-sion is this

Molto tranquillo, ma non lento.

Str.

süss die Won-ne rein-ster Treu-e;
trust doth hal-low joy and love;

Treu', er soll mich's leh-ren! Gen ihn will ich die Waf-fen keh-ren,
love, yea, I will teach thee! The gods of vengeance soon shall reach thee,

lass zu dem Glau - ben dich neu be-
turn then, oh turn to our faith, I be-
cresc.
durch ih - ren Hoch-muth werd' ihr Reu', durch ih - ren
Their wrath de - stroy-ing thou shalt prove, their wrath de-
p
Ped. *
keh - ren: es giebt ein Glück, es giebt ein
seech thee, our faith di - vine, our faith di-
dim. p
Hochmuth werd' ihr Reu'! Gen ihn will ich die Waf - fen keh - ren,
stroy-ing thou shalt prove! The gods of vengeance soon shall reach thee,
dim.
p Wind.
Ped. * Ped. * Ped. *
p ritard. f dim. p pp
Glück, ein Glück, das oh-ne Reu', ein Glück, das oh - ne
vine, Oh turn un-to our faith di-vine, for God is
durch ih - ren Hochmuth werd' ihr Reu', durch ih - ren Hochmuth werd' ihr
their wrath de-stroying thou shalt prove, their wrath de-stroy - ing thou shalt
ritard. p cresc. f dim. p più p
Ped. *

(Ortrud, conducted by
Reu'!
love!
Reu'!
prove!
espressivo.
p Tutti.
legato.
Elsa, with hypocritical reluctance enters through the lower door; the maids precede them with lights,
and, when all have entered, lock the door. Beginning of daybreak.)
mf
dim.
Frederick again advances from back.
più p
pp
B. Cl. & Bssn.
Frederick.
So zieht das Un - heil
The pow'rs of dark - ness

Moderato.

— in dies Haus! Voll-füh-re, Weib, was dei-ne List er-son-nen; dein
— en-ter'd there! Thou god-less one! thy fell re-solve ful-fil thou; no

pp Str.

Ped. * Ped. * Ped.

Werk zu hemmen fühl' ich kei-ne Macht! Das Un-heil hat mit
pow'r have I to hin-der thy in-tent! The ru-in that be-

cresc. fp

mei-nem Fall be-gon-nen, nun stür-zet nach, die mich da-hin ge-
gan with my dis-as-ter, down-ward shall hurl those who a-based me

fp ff fp

Ped. *

bracht! Nur Ei-nes seh' ich mah-nend vor mir
thus! Come life or death, my pur-pose shall not

Trombs & Tb. sustain.

p cresc. fp Str.

steh'n: der Räu-ber mei-ner Eh-re soll ver-
fail, the cause of my dis-hon-or shall not

ff ff ff

Scene III.

Gradual daybreak. Two warders blow the Reveille from the turret, which is answered from another turret in the distance.)

Same score (3 Clarinets in A, Horns in D, Trumpets in D, Kettle Drums in A & D,) afterward Harp.

(Frederick having spied about for the spot most favorable for concealing himself from the populace, steps behind one of the mural projections of the Minster.)

(While the warders descend from the turret and unlock the gates, servitors of the Castle enter from various directions; they salute each other and proceed quietly on their several ways: some draw water at the well, in metal vessels, knock at the entrance of the Palas and are admitted.)

(The gates of the Pal-
Fl. & Ob.
as are opened again, the four Royal Trumpeters issue from them and blow the call.)
poco cresc.
4 Tpts. on the stage.
f
ff
Hns.
f
dim.
(The trumpeters reënter
p
più p
pp
the Palas; the servitors have left the stage.)
(From here the Nobles and the inhabitants of the fortress enter, some
Più mosso.
Tnr.
pp
pp
Hns. & Bssn. sustain.
K. Dr.
from the city road, others from various quarters of the citadel, and in increasing number.)
Vl.
Cello & Vl.

Wind.
p
poco cresc.
Str.
Hns. Bssn. & Tps.
Str.
ff
1st Chorus.
TENOR I.
In Früh'n ver-sam-melt uns der Ruf, gar viel,
The call hath summon'd us be - times, Great deeds,
TENOR II.
BASS I.
In Früh'n ver-sam-melt uns der Ruf, gar viel,
The call hath summon'd us be - times, Great deeds,
BASS II.
2nd Chorus.
TENOR I.
In Früh'n ver-sam-melt uns der Ruf, gar
The call hath sum-mon'd us be - times, Great
TENOR II.
BASS I.
In Früh'n ver-sam-melt uns der Ruf, gar
The call hath sum-mon'd us be - times, Great
BASS II.
Hn. & Bass.
Str. pizz.

gar viel,
great deeds,
gar viel ver-
great deeds this
hei-sset wohl der Tag,
day to us doth bode,
gar viel,
great deeds,
gar viel ver-
great deeds this
hei-sset wohl der Tag,
day to us doth bode,
cresc.
viel,
deeds,
gar
great
viel,
deeds,
gar viel ver-
great deeds this
cresc.
viel,
deeds,
gar
great
viel,
deeds,
gar viel ver-
great deeds this

gar viel!
great deeds!
Der hier so heh-re
Ere high the sun in
gar viel!
great deeds!
Der hier so heh-re Wun-der schuf, der
Ere high the sun in heav-en climbs, Will
Der hier so
Ere high the
hei-sset wohl der Tag,
day to us doth bode,
gar viel!
great deeds!
hei-sset wohl der Tag,
day to us doth bode,
gar viel!
great deeds!
Str. arco
ten. p

Wunder schuf,
heaven climbs,
manch' neu - e That voll-brin-gen mag.
Will much be wrought for ill or good.
theure Held,
much be wrought,
manch' neu - e That voll-brin-gen mag.
will much be wrought for ill or good.
espress.
Der hier so
Ere high the
hehre Wunder schuf,
sun in heaven climbs,
Der hier so heh-re Wun-der schuf,
Ere high the sun in heav-en climbs,
manch' neu - e That voll-brin-gen
Will much be wrought for ill or
Der hier so heh-re Wun-der schuf,
Ere high the sun in heav-en climbs,
manch' neu-e That voll-brin-gen
Will much be wrought for ill or
Str. pizz.

Gar viel ver-hei-sset uns der Tag, der
Great deeds to us this day doth bode, ere
Gar viel verheisst der Tag, der
Great deeds this day doth bode, for
heh-re Wun-der schuf, manch' neu - e That voll -
sun in heav-en climbs, will much be wrought for
Gar viel verheisst der Tag, der
Great deeds this day doth bode, great
mag. Gar viel ver-hei-sset uns der
good. Ere high the sun in heav - en
mag. Gar viel verheisst der
good. This day will much be
mag. Gar viel verheisst der
good. This day will much be
Vl. arco.
p Hns & Bssn.
Tnr. & 'Cello pizz.

sol-che Wunder schuf, manch' neu - e That vollbringen mag; gar
high the sun doth climb, will much be wrought for ill or good; great
Hel - de hier manch' neu - e That vollbrin - gen mag; gar
ill or good, will much be wrought for ill or good; great
brin - gen mag, manch' neu - e That vollbringen mag; gar
ill or good, will much be wrought for ill or good; great
Held heut' manch' neu- -e That voll-bringt; gar
deeds this bright day to us doth bode; great
Tag, manch' neu - e That! Der hier so heh - re Wun - der
climbs, will much be wrought, will much be wrought for ill or
Tag, manch' neu - e That! Gar viel ver - heisst der
wrought, will much be wrought for ill, for ill or
Tag, manch' neu - e That! Der hier so heh - re
wrought, will much be wrought, will much be wrought for
Tag, manch' neu - e That! Gar viel ver - heisst der
wrought, will much be wrought for ill, for ill or

viel verheisset uns der Tag, manch' neu-e That, manch' neu-e
deeds to us this day doth bode, for ill or good, for ill or
viel verheisst der Tag, manch' neu-e That, manch' neu-e
deeds to us doth bode, for ill or good, for ill or
viel verheisst der Tag, manch' neu-e That, gar
deeds to us doth bode, for ill or good, great
viel verheisst der Tag, manch' neu-e That, manch' neu-e
deeds to us doth bode, for ill or good, for ill or
schuf, ganz si-cher manche neu-e That vollbringt;
good, ere high, ere high the sun in heav-en climbs,
Tag; der Held manch' neu-e That voll-bringt;
good, ere high the sun in heav-en climbs,
Wun-der schuf, wohl heut' manch' neu-e That voll-bringt;
ill or good, ere high the sun in heav-en climbs,
Tag; der Held manch' neu-e That voll-bringt;
good, this day, this day will much be wrought,

dolce.
That,
good,
manch' neu - e
for ill or
That!
good!
Der
Ere
That,
good,
manch' neu - e
for ill or
That!
good!
viel ver - heisset uns der Tag;
deeds this day to us doth bode;
der
and
Held wohl man - che neu - e
ere on high the sun in
That,
good;
Ganz ge - wiss,
ere the sun
manch' neu - e
high heaven
That!
climbs,
dolce.
manch' neu - e That!
will much be wrought!
Der
ere
hier so heh -
high the sun
dolce.
manch' neu - e That!
will much be wrought!
Der so heh -
will much, yea,
der hier so heh - re Wun - der schuf,
will much be wrought for ill or good,
manch' neu - e That,
will much be wrought,
ganz ge - wiss!
or for ill,
Ganz ge -
or for
Tnr. & 'Cello arco.

hier so heh- -re Wunder schuf, manch' neu - e_That
high the sun in heaven climbs, will much bewrought,
dolce.
Der solch' Wun- -der schuf, führ-wahr, manch' neu - e That voll -
Yes, much will be wrought, much will be wrought for ill or
That voll-bringt, der hier solch' Wun-der thut, wohl manche
heaven_climbs, this day will much be wrought, this day will
Ganz ge-wiss! Ge - wiss!
Will be wrought or ill
- - re Wun-der, so heh - re Wun - der schuf, manch'
— in heav-en, the sun in heav - en_climbs, will
- re Wunder schuf, manch' neu - e That vollbringt er
— will much be wrought, will much be wrought, for ill, for
heut' man - che neu-e_That voll - bringt; der hier so heh - re_Wun-der
ere high the sun in_heav-en climbs, will much be wrought for ill or
wiss! Manch' neu-e That, manch'
good! yea, on this day will
diminuendo.

cresc.
voll - bringt er heut'.
will much be wrought,
manch'
will
cresc.
bringt er heu - te noch ganz ge-wiss!
good, ere high the sun heav-en climbs!
cresc.
neu - e That voll - bringt er noch heut';
much be wrought for ill or for good!
manch'
this
cresc.
Ge - wiss! Ganz ge-wiss! Manch'
or good! Will be wrought, or
neu - e That, manch' neu - e That er voll-
much be wrought, will much a-mongst us be
heu - te noch, manch' neu - e That er voll-
ill or good, will much amongst us be
cresc.
schuf, wohl manch' neu - e That voll - bringt er heut', manch' neu - e
good, yea, much will be wrought for ill or good, for ill or
cresc.
neu - e That, manch' neu - e That er voll-
much be wrought, for ill, for ill or for
mf
D.Bass arco.

più f
ff
neu - e That_ er voll - bringt, manch' kühne, schö-ne That!
In
much be wrought, or for ill_ or_ good, for ill or good!
The
f
Manch' neu-e That er vollbringt, manch' küh - ne That!
or ill or good, will be wrought, or ill or good!
neu - e That er vollbringt, manch' küh - ne That!
day, for ill or for good, will much be wrought!
neu-e That er vollbringt, manch' küh - ne That!
ill or good, will be wrought, or ill or good!
bringt,
wrought,
Gewiss!
for ill
Ganz gewiss!
or for good!
Gewiss,
That,
good,
Manch' kühne That vollbringt er
for ill, for ill or good will much be
mf

f
Früh'n versammelt uns der Ruf;
call hath summon'd us be-times;
gar viel,
great deeds,
gar viel,
great deeds,
ff
In Früh'n versammelt uns der Ruf;
The call hath summon'd us be-times;
gar viel, gar
great deeds, great
heut'!
wrought.
Hns.
Str.
cresc.

gar viel ver - hei - sset uns der Tag! Gar
great deeds this day to us doth bode! great
gar viel ver - hei - sset uns der Tag! Gar
great deeds this day to us doth bode! great
viel, gar viel ver - hei - sset uns der Tag!
deeds, great deeds this day to us doth bode!
viel, gar viel ver - hei - sset uns der Tag! Gar viel,
deeds, great deeds this day to us doth bode! great deeds
viel verheiss't, gar viel ver-hei-sset uns der Tag! Gar viel,
deeds this day, great deeds this day to us doth bode! great deeds
Hns.
Str.

viel, gar viel!
deeds, great deeds!
viel, gar viel!
deeds, great deeds!
gar viel, gar viel!
this day doth bode!
gar viel, gar viel!
this day doth bode!
(The Herald comes out of the Palace preceded by the four Trumpeters. All turn in anxious expectation towards the back of the scene.)
Hns. & Bssn.
Str.
Tutti.
ff
4 Tps. on the stage.
f
Ped.
Tps. on the stage.
ff

The Herald. (on the elevation before the gates of the Palas.)

Poco più lento.

Des Kö-nigs Wort und Will' thu' ich euch kund; drum ach-tet
Our King's au-gust de-cree through all the lands I here make
wohl, was euch durch mich er sagt!
known: Mark well what he com-mands!
Str.
In Bann und Acht
Be-neath a ban
K. Dr.
Trombs.
ist Fried-rich Tel-ra-mund, weil un-treu er den Got-tes-kampf ge-
he lays Count Tel-ra-mund for tempt-ing Heav'n with trai-tor-ous in-
wagt: wer sein noch pflegt, wer sich zu ihm ge-sellt, nach
tent. Who-e'er shall har-bor or com-pan-ion him, by
Rei-ches Recht der-sel-ben Acht ver-fällt.
right shall share his doom with life and limb.
cresc.

Chorus of Men.
Molto Allegro.
ff
Fluch ihm! Fluch ihm, dem Un-ge-treu-en, den
Curs-ed, ac-curs-ed be the trai-tor, by
Fluch ihm! Fluch ihm, dem Un-ge-treu-en,
Curs-ed, ac-curs-ed be the trai-tor,
Molto Allegro.
Wind.
Str.
Bssn. & Basses.
Got-tes Ur-theil traf! Ihn soll der
us and Heav'n un-blest! He shall be
den Got-tes Ur-theil traf!
by us and Heav'n un-blest!
Rei-ne scheu-en! ihn soll der
held ab-hor-red! he shall be
Ihn soll der Rei-ne scheu-
he shall be held ab-hor-
Rei-ne scheu-en, der Rei-ne scheu-
held ab-hor-red, be held ab-hor-
-en! Ihn soll der Rei-ne scheu-
-red, he shall be held ab-hor-
dim.

en, es flieh' ihn
red, on earth he
en, es flieh' ihn
red, on earth he
più p
p
f
p
ff
Ruh' und Schlaf! Fluch
shall not rest! Ac-
Ruh' und Schlaf! Fluch
shall not rest! Ac-
pp
Wind.
ff
Str.
ihm! Fluch ihm! Fluch ihm, dem Un-ge-treu-en!
curs'd! ac-curs'd! Curs-es up-on the trai-tor!
ihm! Fluch ihm! Fluch ihm, dem Un-ge-treu-en!
curs'd! ac-curs'd! Curs-es up-on the trai-tor!
(At the sound of the trumpets, the people resume their attentive bearing.)
Tutti.
Herald.
Poco più lento.
4 Tpts. on the stage.
Und wei-ter kündet euch der Kö-nig
This further doth the King make known through
Ped.

an, dass er dem frem-den, gott-ge-sand-ten Mann, den El-sa zum Ge-
me: The no-ble stran-ger sent by Heav'n's de-cree, Who El-sa's hand as
Str. p
più p
mah-le sich er-sehnt, mit Land und Kro-ne von Bra-bant be-lehnt. Doch will der
con-sort doth re-quest, With crown and scep-tre doth the King in-vest. The knight doth
cresc.
f
dim.
Held nicht Her-zog sein ge-nannt, ihr sollt ihn hei-ssen: Schü-tzer von Bra-
not as Duke to reign con-sent, But takes for ti-tle: Guard-ian of Bra-
p
più p
Molto allegro.
bant!
bant!
1st Chorus.
Hoch,
Hail,
Hoch, hoch der er-sehn-te Mann!
Hail, hail to the val-iant knight!
Hoch, hoch der er-sehn-te Mann! Heil
Hail, hail to the val-iant knight! all
2nd Chorus.
Heil ihm! Heil! Heil!
All hail! all hail!
Heil ihm! Heil! Heil ihm!
All hail! hail! all hail!
Molto allegro.
Str.
ff
Wind.

Heil ihm, den Gott ge-sandt!
Whom Heav'n its pow'r doth grant!
ihm!
hail!
Heil ihm, den Gott ge-sandt! Heil ihm! Heil ihm, den Gott-ge-
all hail, thou knight of Heav'n, all hail! Whom Heav'n its pow'r doth
cresc.
Wind.
Treu sind wir un-ter-than dem Schützer von Bra-bant!
We vow al-legiance to the Guardian of Bra-bant!
Heil!
Hail!
sandt!
grant!
Treu sind wir un-ter-than dem
We vow al-le-giance to the
Str. stacc.
Heil! Hoch der er-sehn-te Mann!
Hail! Hail, hail, thou knight of Heav'n!
Schützer von Bra-bant!
Guardian of Bra-bant!
Hoch der er-sehn-te
Hail, hail, thou knight of
Hns. & Tpts.
cresc.

ff
Heil ihm, den Gott_ ge - sandt!_ Heil ihm! Heil ihm! Heil
Long reign thou o'er_ Bra - bant!_ All hail! all hail! whom
ff
Mann!
Heav'n!
ff
Heil! Heil ihm, den_ Gott ge - sandt!
Hail! all hail, thou_knight of Heav'n!
ff
Heil ihm, den Gott ge - sandt!
All hail, thou knight of Heav'n!
Wind.
mf cresc.
più f
1st & 2nd Chorus.
ff
Heil ihm, den Gott_ ge - sandt! Heil ihm, dem_ Schützer von Bra - bant!
Heav - en its pow'r_ doth grant! All hail, thou_ Guardian of Bra - bant!
ff
ff
Heil ihm, den Gott ge - sandt! Heil ihm, dem Schützer von Bra - bant! Heil
Heav - en its pow'r doth grant! All hail, thou Guardian of Bra - bant! All
ff
ff
Heil ihm, den Gott ge - sandt! Heil ihm, dem_ Schützer von Bra-bant! Heil ihm!
Heav - en its pow'r doth grant! All hail, thou_ Guardian of Bra-bant! All hail!
ff
ff
Heil, Heil, dem_ Schützer von Bra-bant! Heil,
All hail, thou_ Guardian of Bra-bant! All
ff
ff
Heil ihm! Heil, dem Schützer von Bra-bant! Heil ihm, Heil,
All hail! Hail, thou Guardian of Bra-bant! All hail, all
ff
ihm! Heil, dem Schützer von Bra-bant! Heil ihm! Heil,
hail! Hail, thou Guardian of Bra-bant! All hail! all
ff
Heil, Heil, dem Schützer von Bra-bant! Heil ihm!
Hail, hail, thou Guardian of Bra-bant! All hail!
Wind.
ff
Strs.

rit.
Heil, dem Schützer von Bra - bant!
hail, thou Guardian of Bra - bant!
fp
cresc.
K. Dr.
ff a tempo.
4 Tpts. on the stage. (At the trumpet-call, the people forthwith resume their attentive attitude.)
The Herald.
Nun hört, was Er durch mich euch sa - gen
The knight through me doth furthermore de -
Poco più lento.
4 Tpts. on the stage.
Orchestra.
Tpts. & Trombs.
Str.
lässt: heut' fei - ert er mit euch sein Hochzeit - fest;
clare: All to th'espousals shall this day re - pair;
doch mor - gen sollt ihr
Then straight be un - der
Trombs.

kampf-ge-rüs-tet nah'n, zur Hee-res-folg' dem Kö-nig un-ter-than; er selbst ver-
arms by morning's dawn, And fol-low him till glo-ry's meed be won; In dalliance
fp
p
(with warmth.)
schmäht der süssen Ruh' zu pfle-gen, er führt euch an zu hehren Ruh-mes Se-
soft to lin-ger he dis-dain-eth, While foe or danger to the land re-main-
cresc.
f
Molto Allegro.
(After a short while, the Herald with the four Trumpeters return into the palas.)
gen!
eth!
1st & 2nd Chorus. (with exultation.)
ff
Zum
We
Strei-
fol-
Molto Allegro.
accel. Str.
p Tps. molto cresc.
più f
ff Wind.

ff

- - te säu-met nicht! Zum Strei-te säu-met
- - low where he leads! We fol-low where he

ff

- - te säu-met nicht! Zum Strei-te säu-met nicht, auf! säu-met
- - low where he leads! We fol-low where he leads, wher-e'er he

ff

- - te säu-met nicht! Zum Strei-te säu-met nicht, auf! säu-met
- - low where he leads! We fol-low where he leads, wher-e'er he

ff

te, zum Strei-te säu-met nicht, führt euch der Heh-re an, führt
low, we fol-low where he leads, till glo-ry's meed be won, till

f Str.

ff

nicht, führt euch der Heh - re an! Wer mu - thig
leads, till glo - ry's meed be won! Might - y and

ff

nicht, führt euch der Heh - re an! Wer mu - thig
leads, till glo - ry's meed be won! Might - y and

ff

nicht, führt euch der Heh - re an! Zum Strei-te
leads, till glo - ry's meed be won! We fol-low

ff

euch der Heh - re an! Zum Strei-te säu - met nicht! Zum
glo-ry's meed be won! We fol-low where he leads! We

ff

Ob. Cl. Hns. & Bssn.

stacc.

mit ihm ficht, dem lacht des Ruh-mes Bahn! Auf! säumt zu
gal - lant deed's thro' him shall yet be done! Come, come, we

säu-met nicht führt euch der Heh-re an! Wer mu-thig
where he leads, till glo - ry's meed be won! Come, come, for

Strei - te! Säu - met nicht, führt euch der Heh - re an! Wer
fol - low where he leads, till glo - ry's meed be won! Come,

stacc.

ff
strei - ten nicht, führt euch der Heh - re an! Gott hat ihn ge -
fol - low him till glo - ry's meed be won! Bless - ed are our
ff
strei - ten nicht, führt euch der Heh - re an! Gott hat ihn ge -
fol - low him till glo - ry's meed be won! Bless - ed are our
mit ihm ficht, dem lacht des Ruh - mes Bahn! Gott hat ihn ge -
might - y deeds thro' him shall yet be done! Bless - ed are our
ff
mu - thig mit ihm ficht, dem lacht des Ruh - mes Bahn Von
come, for might - y deeds thro' him shall yet be done! Oh
Str.
f Wind sustain.
sandt zur Grö - sse von Bra - bant! Von
shores, for glo - ry will be ours! Oh
sandt zur Grö - sse von Bra - bant! Von
shores, for glo - ry will be ours! Oh
Gott ist er ge - sandt zur Grö - sse von Bra -
bless - ed are our shores, for glo - ry will be
Gott ist er ge - sandt! von Gott
blest, our hap - py shores, for glo -
Gott ist er ge - sandt! zur Grö - sse von Bra - bant, zur
blest, our hap - py shores, for glo - ry shall be ours, for
Gott ist er ge - sandt! zur Grö - sse von Bra - bant, zur
blest, our hap - py shores, for glo - ry shall be ours, for
bant, ja, von Gott ist er ge - sandt, ja, von Gott zur
ours, blest, oh blest our hap - py shores, blest, for ev - er
più f

12946

ist er uns da-her ge-sandt!
-ry, for glo-ry shall be ours!
Wer muthig mit ihm
Thro' him shall yet be
Grö-sse, zur Grö-sse von Bra-bant!
glo-ry, for glo-ry shall be ours!
Grö-sse von Bra-bant!
glo-ry shall be ours!
Wer mu-thig mit ihm ficht, dem
Might-y and gal-lant deeds through
Grö-sse von Bra-bant!
blest our hap-py shores!
Wer mu-thig mit ihm ficht, dem
Might-y and gal-lant deeds through
Hns. & Bssn.
stacc.
ficht,
done,
dem lacht des Ruh-mes Bahn!
thro' him shall yet be done,
Wer mu-thig mit ihm ficht,
thro' him shall yet be done,
dem lacht des Ruh-mes
thro' him shall yet be
lacht des Ruh-mes Bahn!
him shall yet be done!
Auf! säumt zu
might-y and
Drum säu-met nicht zu strei-ten, säu-met nicht! Von
We fol-low where he leads us, yea, we come! Oh
Bahn!
done!
Drum säu-met nicht zum Streit, säu-met nicht!
We fol-low where he leads, yea, we come!
strei-ten nicht, führt euch der Heh-re an!
gal-lant deeds through him shall yet be done!
Str.

Gott ist er ge- sandt zur Grö - sse von Bra - bant; von Gott ist er ge- sandt zur Grö - sse von Bra - bant!
blest our hap-py shores, for glo - ry will be ours, oh blest our hap-py shores, for glo - ry will be ours!
Gott hat ihn ge- sandt zur Grö sse von Bra - bant;
Blest our hap-py shores, for glo - ry will be ours,
Wer mu - thig
Mighty - y and
Säu - met nicht!
Yea, we come!
Auf! säu-met
Might - y and
Auf! säumt zu
Might - y and
molto cresc.
semp.
Wind.

mit ihm ficht, dem lacht des Ruh - mes Bahn, des Ruh - mes
gal - lant deeds thro' him shall yet be done, shall yet be

Wer mu - thig mit ihm ficht, dem
Might - y and gal - lant deeds thro'

nicht zu strei - ten, führt er euch an!
gal - lant deeds thro' him shall be done!

strei - ten nicht, führt euch der Heh - re an! Auf! säu - met
gal - lant deeds thro' him shall yet be done! We come, we

Bahn! Wer mu - thig
done! Might - y and

lacht des Ruh - mes Bahn, dem lacht, dem lacht des Ruh - mes
him shall yet be done, yea, might - y deeds shall yet be

Wer mu - thig mit ihm ficht, dem lacht des Ruh - mes
Might - y and gal - lant deeds thro' him shall yet be

nicht, führt er euch an! Zu strei - ten säu - met
come, wher - e'er he leads! For might - y deeds thro'

mit ihm ficht, dem lacht des Ruh - mes
gal - lant deeds shall yet thro' him be

Bahn, des Ruh - mes Bahn; wer mu - thig mit ihm
done, yea, might - y deeds thro' him shall yet be

Bahn, des Ruh - mes Bahn; wer mu - thig mit ihm
done, yea, might - y deeds thro' him shall yet be

nicht, führt er euch an; säu - met nicht! Säu - met
him shall yet be done, yea, we come! Might - y

Chorus I.
Bahn, dem lacht, dem lacht des Ruh-mes Bahn!
done, yea, might-y deeds shall yet be done!
Von Gott,
We come,
ficht, dem lacht des Ruh-mes heh-re Bahn!
done, yea, might-y deeds shall yet be done!
Chorus II.
ficht, dem lacht des Ruh-mes heh-re Bahn!
done, yea, might-y deeds shall yet be done!
Von
We
nicht, führt euch der Heh-re an!
deeds thro' him shall yet be done!
p Str.
von Gott ist er ge-
we come, wher-e'er he
Gott, von Gott
come, we come,
cresc.
sandt zur Grö-sse von Bra-
leads, to great and gal-lant
ist er ge-sandt, von
wher-e'er he leads, to

ff
bant, von Gott ist er ge - sandt zur Grö - sse von Bra -
deeds, We fol - low where he leads, to great and gal - lant
ff
Gott ist er ge - sandt zur Grö - sse von Bra - bant, von
great and gal - lant deeds, We fol - low where he leads, we
f Wind.
più f
bant, ja, von Gott zur Grö - sse von Bra - bant, von Gott, ja, von
deeds, yea, we come, we fol - low where he leads, we come, yea, we
Gott, ja, von Gott ist er ge - sandt zur Grö - sse von Bra - bant, ja, von
fol - low, to great and gal - lant deeds, to great and gal - lant deeds, yea, we
Both Choruses.
Gott ge - sandt zur Grö - - sse von Bra - bant von
fol - low where he leads, to gal - lant deeds, we
Gott ist er ge - sandt zur Grö - sse von Bra - bant
fol - low where he leads, to great and gal - lant deeds,
Gott ist er ge - sandt zur Grö - sse von Bra - bant von
fol - low where he leads, to great and gal - lant deeds, we

ff
Gott, von Gott ist er ge - sandt!
come, we come, we fol - low him!
Gott, von Gott ist er ge - sandt!
come, we come, we fol - low him!
Tutti.
(While the people are surging in joyful tumult, four Nobles, former lieges of Frederick, come to the front, and stand together.)
Four Nobles. (to one another)
3rd Noble. (BASS I.)
Nun hört! dem
Ye heard! the
Bass.
ff dim.
Str.
Hns. & Bassn. sustain.
2nd Noble. (TENOR II.)
Lan - de will er uns ent - füh - ren? Gen ei - nen Feind, der uns noch nie be -
land we are to quit to - mor - row! Against a foe who nev - er threaten'd

4th Noble. (BASS II.)
droht? Solch' kühn Be-gin-nen sollt' ihm nicht ge-
us! Such bold be-gin-ing yet shall bring him
cresc.
fp
(Frederick has meanwhile approached them unperceived.)
1st Noble. (TENOR I.)
büh-ren! Wer weh-ret ihm, wenn er die Fahrt ge-
sor-row! But who would dare what he commands, re-
cresc.
p
Frederick.
(He uncovers his head, they start back affrighted.)
bot? Ich!
fuse? I!
The Four Nobles.
ff
Ha! Wer bist du? Friedrich!
Ah! who art thou? Fred'rick!
Ha! Wer bist du? Friedrich! Seh' ich
Ah! who art thou? Fred'rick! Oh be-
cresc.
f dim.
p
f
Frederick.
Gar
I
Du wagst dich her, zur Beu-te je-dem Knecht?
If thou art seen, thy life they will not spare!
Du wagst dich her, zur Beu-te je-dem Knecht?
If thou art seen, thy life they will not spare!
recht? Hier wagst du dich her?
ware! Thy life they'll not spare!
p
cresc.
più f
Cl., Bssn. & Basses.

bald will ich wohl wei-ter noch mich wa-gen, vor eu-ern
fear not, and ere long I'll un-de- -ceive ye, For true and
ffp Str.
Au-gen soll es leuch-tend ta-gen! Der euch so kühn die
sackless ye shall yet be-lieve me! He who for war un-
f
Heerfahrt an-ge-sagt, der sei von mir des Got- -tes-trugs be-
just your swords would task, I will this day as re- -cre-ant knight un-
f
p
cresc.
ff
(Four Pages issue from the door of the Kemenate upon the balcony; they gaily run down the staircase and stand before the doorway of the Palas.)
klagt!
mask!
1st & 2nd Noble.
Was hör ich!
What say'st thou?
Was hast du vor?
What wilt thou do?
Weh' dir
If seen
3rd Noble.
Was hör ich!
What say'st thou?
Was hast du vor? Ver-lor'- ner du,
What wilt thou do? what mad - ness, this!
4th Noble.
Ra- sen-der!
Mad- man, thou!
Was hast du vor? Ver-
What wilt thou do? Thy
Str.
Bssn. stacc.

(The Nobles urge Frederick towards the Minster, where they endeavor to conceal him from the populace.)
hört dich des Vol - kes Ohr!
thou shalt thy rash - ness rue.
hört dich des Vol - kes Ohr!
thou shalt thy rash - ness rue.
lor' - ner, hört dich das Volk!
rash - ness soon thou wilt rue!
cresc.
(The populace, perceiving the Pages, crowd towards the front.)
poco cresc.
più cresc.
Str. & Tpts.
Four Pages. (on the terrace before the Palas.)
Macht Platz!
Make way!
Macht Platz!
Make way!
stacc.
Vl.
Wind.
stacc.

für El - sa, un - sre Frau:
Our La - dy El - sa comes,
die will in Gott zum Mün - ster
un - to the Min - ster she goes
dim.
più p
pp
dim. p
(They come down the stage, opening a wide passage through the readily yielding nobles to
geh'n.
forth.
Vl.
poco a poco rall.
cresc.
f dim.
the steps of the Minster, where they take their stand.)
Andante.
p Cl.&Fl.
più p
Wind.
(Four other Pages come with measured steps from the upper door of the Kemenate, and stand on the balcony, awaiting the train of Ladies which they are to accompany.)
Hp.

Fourth Scene.

Same Score (Cl. in B♭, Hns. in E flat), except Hp.

(A long train of ladies, magnificently attired, proceeds slowly from the Kemenate, passing before the Palas (L.H.); then, returning to the front, they ascend the steps of the Minster, where the first-comers arrange themselves.)

Chorus I.
TENOR.
pp
Ge - seg - net soll sie schrei - ten, die lang' in
May ev - 'ry joy at - tend thee, Who long in
BASS.
pp
TENOR.
pp
Ge - seg - net soll sie
May ev - 'ry joy at -
Chorus II.
BASS.
pp
Vl.
mf
dim.
Str.
p
De - muth litt.
grief wert bound,
p
Gott mö - ge sie ge - lei - ten,
May Heav'n its blessing lend thee,
p
schrei - ten, die lang' in De - muth litt;
tend thee, Who long in grief wert bound,
p
Gott
May
p
p

Gott hü - te ih - ren Schritt!
And an - gels guard thee round!

mö - ge sie ge - lei - ten, Gott
Heav'n its bless - ing lend thee, And

Ped. * Ped. *

(The Nobles, who have involuntarily pressed forward again, here make way for the Pages, who clear the road for the train which by this time has arrived before the Palas.)

(Here Elsa has reached

Sie naht,
She comes,

hü - te ih - ren Schritt!
an - gels guard thee round!

Vl.

più p

pp

Wind sustain.

Ped. * Ped. * Ped. *

the terrace of the Palas; the way is again clear, so that all can see her. She remains awhile

keu - - - - scher
hol - - - -y
keu - - scher
ho - -ly
Gluth
thoughts
ent -
in -
von
On
keu - - scher
ho - - ly
von
On
keu - scher
ho - ly
(From here Elsa proceeds slowly to the front, through the path left open by the men.)
brannt!
tent!
Heil dir!
All hail!
Gluth
thoughts
ent - brannt!
in - tent!
Gluth
thoughts
ent - brannt!
in - tent!
Heil dir, o
Thine be a
Wood.

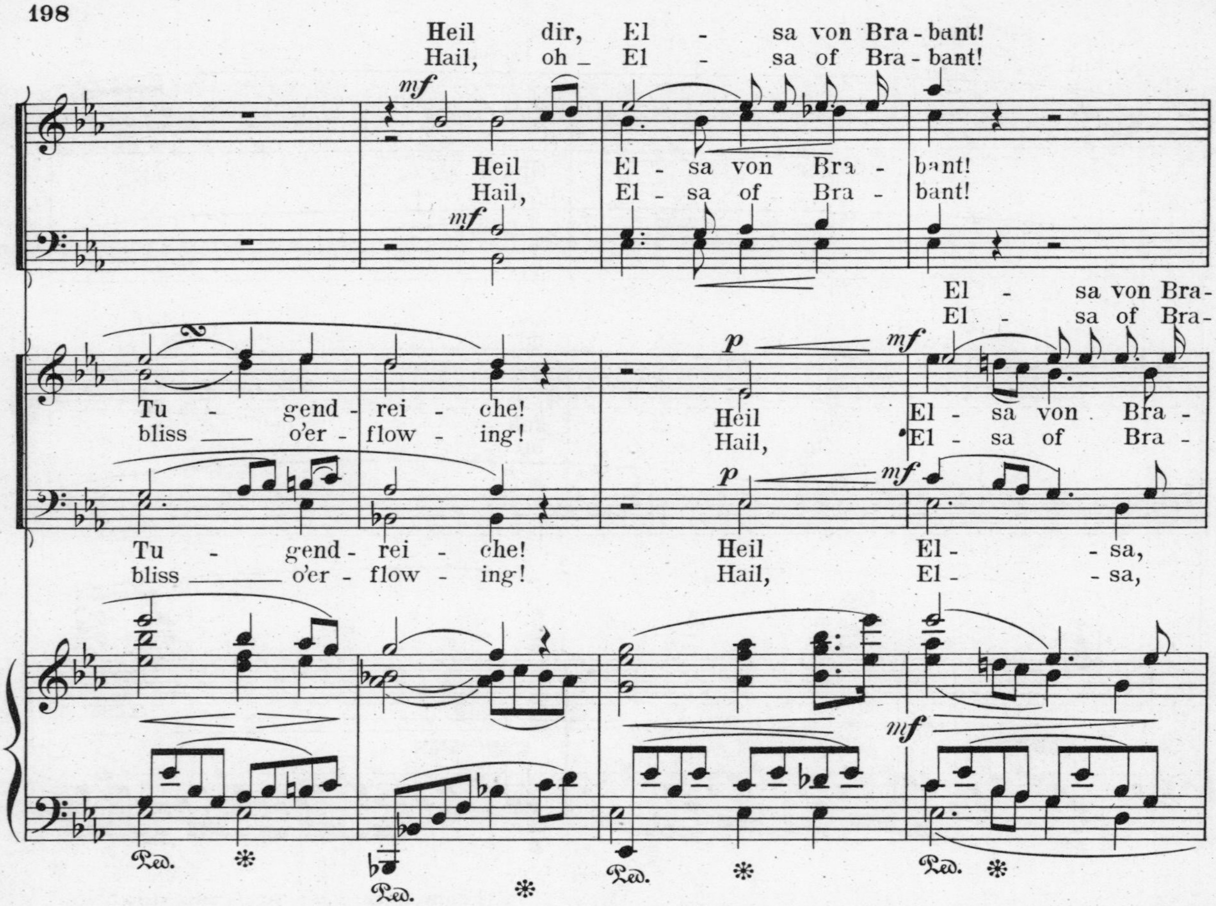

Heil dir, El - sa von Bra-bant!
Hail, oh El - sa of Bra-bant!

Heil El-sa von Bra-bant!
Hail, El-sa of Bra-bant!

El - sa von Bra-
El - sa of Bra-

Tu - gend-rei - che!
bliss o'er - flow - ing!

Heil El - sa von Bra-
Hail, El - sa of Bra-

Tu - gend-rei - che!
bliss o'er - flow - ing!

Heil El - sa,
Hail, El - sa,

(Here, besides the Pages, the foremost Ladies have reached the steps of the Minster, where they stand aside to let Elsa pass into the Church before them.)

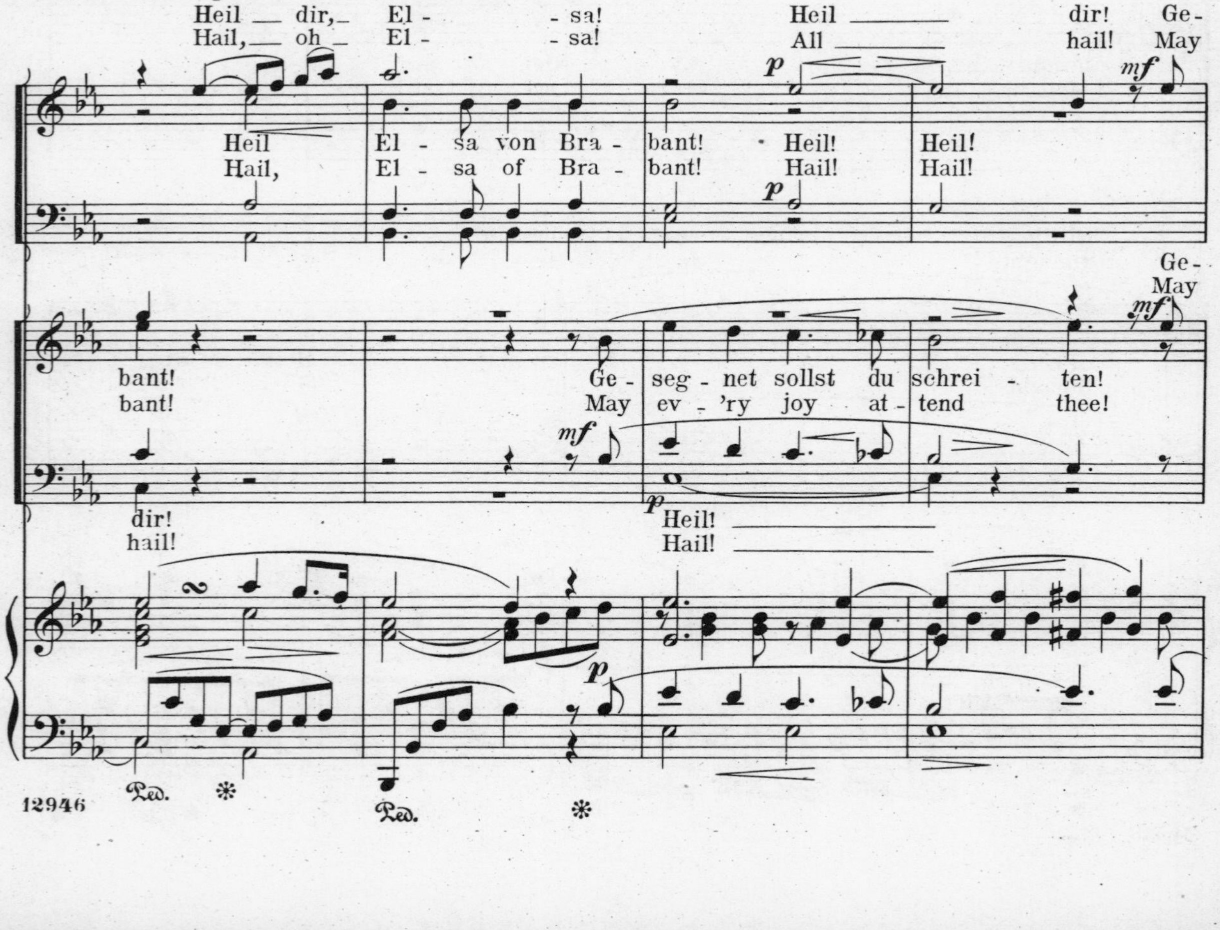

Heil dir, El - sa! Heil dir! Ge-
Hail, oh El - sa! All hail! May

Heil El - sa von Bra - bant! Heil! Heil!
Hail, El - sa of Bra - bant! Hail! Hail!

Ge-
May

bant! Ge - seg - net sollst du schrei - ten!
bant! May ev - 'ry joy at - tend thee!

dir! Heil!
hail! Hail!

SOPRANO.

Heil dir, Tugendreiche, Heil dir, Tugendreiche, Heil Elsa von Bra-

Thine be bliss o'erflowing, Thine be bliss o'erflowing, Hail, Elsa of Bra-

ALTO.

Heil dir! Gesegnet sollst du schreiten! Heil! Heil Elsa von Brabant! Heil Elsa von Bra-

All hail! May ev'ry joy attend thee! Hail, Hail, Elsa of Brabant! Hail, Elsa of Bra-

TENOR I.

segnet sollst du schreiten! Heil Elsa von Brabant! Heil Elsa von Brabant! Heil Elsa von Bra-

ev'ry joy attend thee! Hail! Elsa of Brabant! Hail, Elsa of Brabant! Hail, Elsa of Bra-

TENOR II.

Heil Elsa von Brabant! Heil! Heil Elsa von Brabant! Heil Elsa von Bra-

Hail! Elsa of Brabant! Hail, Hail, Elsa of Brabant! Hail, Elsa of Bra-

BASS I.

Heil dir, Elsa von Brabant! Heil dir! Ja, gesegnet sollst du schreiten, Gott möge dich geleiten!

Hail, oh Elsa of Brabant! All hail! oh, may ev'ry joy attend thee, May Heav'n its blessing lend thee!

BASS II.

Heil Elsa von Brabant!

Hail! Elsa of Brabant!

cresc. *più cresc.*

più f
bant! Heil! Heil! Heil dir! Heil
bant! Hail! Hail! All hail! oh,
bant! Heil! Heil! Heil dir! Heil
bant! Hail! hail! All hail! oh,
bant! Heil! Heil! Heil dir! Heil
bant! Hail! Hail! All hail! oh,
Heil dir, Tu - gend - rei - che! Heil! Heil dir! Heil
Thine be bliss o'er - flow - ing! Hail! All hail! oh,
molto cresc.
ff
(As Elsa places her foot on the second step of the Minster, Ortrud, who till now has been at the rear of the train of Ladies, hastily comes forward, and places herself on the same step, thus confronting Elsa.)
Allegro con fuoco.
El - sa von Bra - bant!
El - sa of Bra - bant!
Allegro con fuoco.
Str.

Ortrud.
Zu - rück, El - sa! Nicht länger will ich
Stand back, El - sa! No longer will I
Wind.
Str.
dul - den, dass ich gleich einer Magd dir folgen soll!
bear it, That I like an - y slave must follow thee!
Den Vor - tritt
'Tis I pre -
sollst du ü - ber - all mir schulden,
cede, to all I here de - clare it,
vor mir dich beu - gen sollst du de - muth -
And thou shalt hum - bly bow thy head to
sostenuto
Ob. & Hns.
Wind.
Vivo.
Elsa (greatly startled.)
voll!
me!
Um Gott!
Great Heav'n,
Was muss ich
what doth she
The Eight Pages.
Was will das Weib?
What doth she mean?
Chorus.
TENORS.
Was will das Weib?
What doth she mean?
Zu -
Stand
BASSES.
Was will das
What doth she
Was will das Weib?
What doth she mean?
Vivo.
Str.

sehn? Welch jä - her Wech - sel ist mit dir ge -
mean? How chang'd thy tone, who late to me did
(They push Ortrud back to the centre of the stage.)
rück!
back!
Weib?
mean?
3 Bssn.
dim.
p
Ortrud.
schehn? Weil ei-ne Stund' ich meines Werth's ver-ges-sen, glau - best
sue! If I one hour was of my worth un - mind-ful, Think thou
p
fp
Cello.
Ob.
du, ich mü-sste dir nur krie - chend nahn? Mein
not, that I be-fore thy feet will cow'r! An
cresc.
con molta forza
Leid zu rä-chen, will ich mich ver-mes-sen, was mir ge - bührt, das
am - ple vengeance thy dis-dain doth owe me, My right-ful rank I
f
fp
fp
fp
Wind.

(general amazement and commotion.)
will ich nun em-pfah'n!
will as-sert this hour!
Str.
ff
Elsa.
Weh! liess ich durch dein Heu-cheln mich ver-lei-ten,
Woe! was it naught but false-hood to mis-lead me,
Wind.
p
die die-se Nacht sich jammernd zu mir stahl? Wie willst du
Last night, that brought thee wail-ing to my door? Now thou wouldst
cresc.
fp Wind.
nun in Hoch-muth vor mir schrei-ten, du, ei-nes Gott-ge-
fain at-tempt to su-per-sede me, Thou, mate of one whom
Str.
p
ffp
ff
Ortrud (haughtily, but feigning to be deeply hurt.)
rich-te-ten Gemahl?
God and man forswore?
Wind.
ff
Tnr.
ff
dim.
Str.

quasi a tempo
Wenn falsch Ge-richt mir den Ge-mahl ver-bann-te,
Through doom un-just o'er him the ban was spok-en,
Trombs.
pp
Str.
'Cello.
war doch sein Nam' im Lan-de hoch ge-ehrt; als
But his re-nown was great throughout the land; His
p
al-ler Tu-gend Preis man ihn nur nann-te, ge-kannt, ge-
name of virtue's self was held the to-ken, Both fear and
p
fürch-tet war sein tapf'-res Schwert. Der Dei-ne, sag! wer soll-te
hon-or did his sword com-mand. Yon stran-ger, say, as what dost
p
pp
hier ihn ken-nen, ver-magst du selbst den Na-men nicht zu
thou pro-claim him? If I have heard a-right, thou canst not
f

più mosso.

nen - nen!
name him!

Chorus.
The Ladies & Pages. SOPRANO & ALTO.

f Sie lä - stert!
Thou slan - d'rer!

The Men. TENOR. *f*
Ha, was thut sie kund?
Why doth she com - plain?

BASS. *f*
Was sagt sie?
What saith she?

più mosso.
f *Tutti.*

Ortrud. (not dragging.)
Kannst du ihn nen - nen,
Say, canst thou name him,

f Weh - ret ih - rem Mund!
Stay her tongue pro - fane!

Weh - ret ih - rem Mund!
Stay her tongue pro - fane!

f *f*
Weh - ret ih - rem Mund!
Stay her tongue pro - fane!

Wind. *ff* *p Str.*
Ped. *

kannst du uns es sa - gen, ob sein Ge - schlecht, sein A - del wohl be -
who dost so a - dore him? What is his race, his lineage dost thou

fp *pp*

währt? Wo-her die Flu-then ihn zu dir ge-tra-gen,
know? Ere thro' the wa-ters strange enchantment bore him,
wann und wo-hin er wie-der von dir fährt? Ha, nein!
Where was his home? when back is he to go? Ah, no!
cresc.
con molta forza
(più rallentando)
Wohl bräch-te ihm es schlim-me Noth, der klu-ge Held die
That he would have for ev-er hid, The craft-y knight all
Wind.
dim.
Str.
Fra-ge drum ver-bot.
ques-tion-ing for-bade.
Vivo.
SOPRANO.
Sie schmä-het ihn;
Re-vile him not,
ALTO.
Ha, spricht sie wahr?
Can this be true?
Sie
Re-
TENOR.
Sie schmähet ihn!
Re-vile him not!
BASS.
Ha!
Ah!
Welch' schwe-re
A bold as-
Vivo.
più f

Elsa (recovering from her amazement.)
Du
Thou
darf sie es wa - gen?
all is per - ver - sion!
schmä - het ihn; darf sie es wa - gen?
vile him not, all is per - ver - sion!
Darf sie das wa - gen?
All is per - ver - sion!
Darf sie das wa - gen?
All is per - ver - sion!
Kla - gen! Darf sie das wa - gen?
ser - tion! All is per - ver - sion!
ff
ff Wind.
Lä - ste - rin! Ruch - lo - se Frau! Hör', ob ich Ant -
slan - der - er! taunt me no more! Let my re - ply
Str.
(with great warmth.)
-wort mir ge - trau'! So rein und e - del
all doubts as - sure! So pure and no - ble
p
p cresc.
Tpts.
f
p Wind.

ist sein We - sen, so tu - gend -
is his na - ture, As none can
reich der hch - re Mann, dass
match in high re - nown; Oh,
nie des Un - heils soll ge -
can there live so vile a
ne - sen, wer sei - ner Sen - dung
crea - ture, as to as - perse all
zwei - feln kann! Hat nicht durch
hon - or's crown? Hath not as
The Men.
BASS.
TENOR.
Ge-wiss! Ge-wiss!
'Tis true! 'Tis true!

Gott im Kampf geschla - - -
vic - - tor Heav'n de-clar'd

gen mein theu - rer Held den Gat - ten
him, When he the rec - - reant knight o'er -

dein? (to the People.) Nun sollt nach Recht ihr
threw? Ye saw his tri - umph,

Al - le sa - gen, wer
yet he spar'd him; Say,

kann da nur der Rei - ne
lieg - es, can ye doubt him

f Tutti.

sein?
true?
SOPRANO & ALTO.
Dein Held al-
We know him
TENOR.
Nur er! Dein Held al-
No, no, We know him
BASS.
Nur er! Dein Held al-
No, no! We know him
lein!
true!
Ortrud.
Ha!
Ha!
Str.
(mockingly to Elsa.)
die-se Rei-ne dei-nes Hel-den,
though so dough-ty, pure and no-ble,

wie wä - re sie so bald ge - trübt,
If all his mag - ic arts were known,
più p
müsst' er des Zau - bers We - sen mel - den,
Thy pride were turn'd to shame and troub - le,
pp
f
dim.
durch den hier sol - che Macht er übt!
Thou thy cham - pion must soon dis - own!
p
f
p
f
Wagst du ihn nicht dar - um zu fra - gen,
Dost thou not dare his name to ask him,
fp
f
p
(emphatically.)
so glau - ben Al - le wir mit Recht,
We will the truth in - fer by right,
f
p
f
dim.

du müs - sest selbst in Sor - ge za - gen,
An im - pious trai - tor we'll un - mask him,
um sei - ne Rei - - ne steh' es schlecht!
That all may know him recreant knight.
(The gates of the Palas
Tutti.
The Ladies (supporting Elsa.)
Helft ihr vor der Ver - ruch - ten
Res - cue her from this fu - ry's
open; the four Royal Trumpeters pass through them and come forward, blowing.)
Hass!
tongue!
(looking towards the back.)
The Men.
Macht Platz! Der Kö - nig naht!
Make way! The King is near!
Macht Platz! Macht Platz! Der Kö - nig!
Make way! Make way! Our sov'reign!
4 Tpts. on the stage.

Fifth Scene.

Same Score, afterwards Organ.

The King, Lohengrin, and the Saxon Counts and Nobles have issued from the Palas in stately procession; the commotion in front interrupts the train; the King and Lohengrin come forward hastily.

wagt es hier den Kir-chen-gang zu stö - ren?
dares to clamor here with words un - seem - ly?
The Train of the King.
ff
Welcher Streit, den wir ver-nah-men?
We have heard the voice of an-ger.
fp
cresc.
Lohengrin. (perceiving Ortrud.)
Was seh' ich! Das un-sel'-ge Weib bei dir?
Oh hor-ror! Why this e-vil one with thee?
Elsa.
Mein Ret-ter! Schü - tze mich vor die-ser Frau!
My cham-pion! Shel - ter me a-gainst her wrath!
Wind.
Str.
Ob.
p
f
dim.

Schilt mich, wenn ich dir un - ge-hor-sam war! In
Blame me, if I o - bey'd not thy com - mand! I

p *f* *ff dim.*

Jam - mer sah ich sie vor die-ser Pfor-te, aus ih-rer Noth nahm ich sie bei mir
heard her weep-ing sore by yon-der por-tal, and in com - pas-sion har-bor'd her this

p *fp*

auf: nun sieh', wie furcht-bar sie mir lohnt die Gü-te, – sie
night: and now, with harsh and bit - ter words of ha-tred, she

f *p*

poco riten. *p* **Slower.**

Lohengrin. (fixing his eyes commandingly on Ortrud, who stands transfixed.)

schilt mich, dass ich dir zu sehr ver - trau'! Du
taunts me for my bound-less trust in thee! A -

Wind. *più p* *pp* *p B. Cl.* *K. Dr.*

fürch-ter-li-ches Weib, steh' ab von ihr! Hier wird dir nim-mer Sieg! –
way from her, thou fiend, in vain thy arts! Thou hast no part in her!

espress. *Ob.* *più p* *Trombs.* *pp* *p*

Ped. * Ped.

(he turns to Elsa, gently.)
(Elsa, weeping, hides her face on his breast.)
Sag', El - sa, mir, vermocht' ihr Gift sie in dein Herz zu gie - ssen?
El - sa, oh say, hath she had pow'r to taint thy heart with doubt - ing?
Ob.
p
Str.
(Lohengrin, raising her and pointing to the Minster.)
Komm', lass in Freu - de dort die - se Thrä - nen flie -
Come, where in joy thy tears shall dis - solve and van -
f
Wind.
mf
(Lohengrin, Elsa and the King turn towards the Minster followed by their train, who arrange themselves in order.)
ssen!
ish!
Moderato e solenne.
Wind.
Vl.
Str.
cresc.
riten.
più f
(Frederick comes forward on the steps of the Minster; the Ladies and Pages shrink from him in terror.)
Frederick.
Agitato.
O Kö - nig! Trug - bethörte
Great Hen - ry! Oh de - lud - ed
Tutti.
ff
p K. Dr.
Ped.

Fürsten!
Princes!

Hal - tet ein!
Nay, de - sist!

All the Men. TENOR I.

f

Was will der
Hence, or be -

TENOR II.

BASS I.

BASS II.

f

Was will der hier?
Hence, or be-ware!

ff *Str.* *fp*

Wind.

fp

cresc.

The King.

Was will der hier?
What doth he here?

hier? Ver - fluch - ter!
ware! Thou trai - tor!

f

Was will der hier? Ver-fluch - ter!
Hence, or be-ware! Thou trai - tor!

f

Was will der hier? Ver-fluch - ter!
Hence, or be-ware! Thou trai - tor!

Was will der hier? Ver-fluch - ter!
hence, or be - ware! Thou trai - tor!

sempre *cresc.* - - - -

Frederick.
O hört mich an!
Oh King, give ear!
The King.
Zu-
A-
Weich' von dan-nen!
Hence, I warn thee!
Zu-
A-
Weich' von dan-nen!
Hence, I warn thee!
Hin-weg!
A-vaunt!
Weich' von dan-nen!
Hence, I warn thee!
Hin-weg!
A-vaunt!
Hin-weg!
A-vaunt!
più f
rück! Wei-che von dan-nen!
vaunt! Hence, thou ac-curs'd one!
Frederick.
Hört mich, dem
Hear me, ye
rück! Du bist des To-des, Mann!
vaunt! Or of thy life be-ware!
Du bist des To-des, Mann!
Or of thy life be-ware!
Du bist des To-des, Mann!
Or of thy life be-ware!
Hin-weg! Des To-des bist du, Mann!
A-vaunt! Or trem-ble for thy life!
Trombs. sustain.
ff
p
Ped.
*

grim - mes Un-recht ihr ge-than!
all have done me grievous wrong!
The King.
Hin-weg!
Stand back!
Weich' von dannen!
Hence, or tremble!
Weich' von dannen!
Hence, or tremble!
Hin - weg!
Stand back!
Weich' von dannen!
Hence, or tremble!
Str.
più f
cresc.
K.Dr.
Got - tes Ge-richt, es ward ent-ehrt, be-tro-gen! Durch ei-nes Zaub'rers
Heav'n's dread or-deal hath he pro-fan'd, de-rid-ed, Thro' sorc'ry vile its
ffp
Trombs.&Tpts.
ff

The King.
List seid ihr be - tro - gen!
judg-ment was mis-guid - ed!
Greift den Ver-
Seize the ac-
Greift den Ver - ruch - ten!
Seize the ac - curs'd one!
Greift den Ver - ruch - ten!
Seize the ac - curs'd one!
Greift den Ver - ruch - ten! Hört!
Seize the ac - curs'd one! Hark!
Str.
ff
Ped.
ruch - ten!
curs'd one!
Hört! Er lästert Gott!
Hark! how he blasphemes!
Hört! Er lästert Gott!
Hark! how he blas - phemes!
Hört! Er lästert Gott!
Hark! how he blas - phemes!
Er lästert Gott!
how he blasphemes!
(They close upon him from all sides.)
poco ritard.
Ped.

Frederick (with a terrible effort to make himself heard, fixes his gaze on Lohengrin only, without noticing the others).

ff
Den dort im Glanz ich vor mir
Yon shin - ing knight, my sword de-
sempre ff
lento.
(The throng shrinks back from Frederick; all listen attentively.)
se - he, den kla-ge ich des Zau - bers an! Wie
fy - ing, I here accuse of sor-c'ry vile! Like
K. Dr.
ff
Trombs.
Staub vor Got-tes Hauch ver - we - he die Macht, die er durch List ge -
dust be-fore the breez-es fly - ing, The pow'r shall be, he won by
p Str.
f
ff
wann! Wie schlecht ihr des Ge-rich - tes wahr - tet,
guile! How ill ye the or-de - al ward - ed,
Vl.& Tnr. dim.
p
das doch die Eh - re mir be - nahm, da ei - ne
When I of hon - or was be - reft, When ye one
p cresc.
f
dim.

Frag' ihr ihm er-spar-tet, als er zum
fa - tal ques - tion spar'd him, That had the
p
cresc.
Got-teskam-pfe kam! Die
spell a-sun - der cleft! If
f
più f
Fra - ge nun sollt ihr nicht weh-ren, dass sie ihm jetzt von mir ge-
guilt - y, here I will un-mask him, My questions none shall dare gain-
ff
Trombs.
f Wind.
f
(with a commanding gesture.)
stellt: nach Na-men, Stand' und Eh-ren
say: His sta-tion, name, I ask him,
Trombs.& Tb.
f
f
f
(A general movement of consternation.)
frag' ich ihn laut vor al-ler Welt!
Let these be heard in light of day!
Tutti.
ff Tpts. added.
pp
cresc.-

Cello, Tnr. & Trombs.
Wer ist er, der an's Land geschwommen, ge - zo - gen von ei - nem wil - den
Who is he, that the bil - lows tid - ed, A swan leading him in pinnace
Tb. & D. Bass.
più p
Schwan?
frail?
Tutti.
cresc.
Wem sol - che Zau - ber - thie - re frommen, des' Rein - heit ach - te ich für
With such fa - mi - liars who - so bid - eth, All hon - est men may well as -
Wahn!
sail!
Nun soll der Klag' er
Jus - tice he now shall
cresc.
Trombs. & Tpts.

Animato.
Re - de stehn; ver-mag er's, so geschah mir
foil no more; Con-demn me, if he prove his
ff
Str.
Recht, wo nicht, so sol-let ihr er-
cause; If not, on him let vengeance
ff
sehn, um sei-ne Rei - ne steh' es
fall, A knight dis-hon - or'd, by our
p
cresc.
f
ff
Allegro.
(all look disturbed and expectantly towards Lohengrin.)
schlecht!
laws!
Chorus of Men.
Welch' har - te
What dread as -
Welch' har - - te
What dread as -
Welch' har te Kla - - - gen!
What dread as-per - - - sion!
Allegro.
f

The King.

Welch' har - te Kla - - gen!
What dread as - per - - sion!

The Ladies & Pages.

Was wird er ihm ent - geg - nen?
Ah! how will he re - fute it?

Welch' har - te Kla - gen!
What dread as - per - sion!

Welch' har - te Kla - gen! Was wird er ent - geg - nen?
What dread as - per - sion! How will he re - fute it?

Kla - gen! Was wird er ihm ent - geg - nen?
per - sion! Oh how will he re - fute it?

Kla - - gen! Was wird er ihm ent - geg - - nen?
per - - sion! Oh how will he re - fute it?

Was wird er ihm nun ent - geg - - nen?
What will he say to re - fute it?

più *f*

Lohengrin.

Nicht dir, der so ver - gass der Eh - ren,
Not thou, base knight, may'st here im - peach me,

Wind.

ff

Ped. *

hab' Noth ich Re - de hier zu steh'n! Des
Whose cra - ven false - hood Heav'n hath shown; No

f

ff

Ped. *

Bö - sen Zwei-fel darf ich weh - ren, vor ihm wird Rei - ne
doubts of e - vil men can reach me, Nor can they tar - nish

Frederick.

nie ver-gehn! Darf
my re - nown! I

Str.

ich ihm nicht als wür - dig gel - ten, dich ruf' ich,
hurl thee back the vile sug - ges - tion, And up - on

Wind. *Str.* *Wind.*

Kö - nig hoch - ge - ehrt! Wird er auch dich un - ad - lig
thee, oh King, I call! Will he pre - sume thy right to

Str. *Wind.* *Str.*

schel - ten, dass er die Fra - ge dir ver - wehrt?
ques - tion, If me he scorns as base - born thrall?

Lohengrin.
Ja, selbst dem Kö - nig darf ich
Yea, e'en the King shall not com-
più f
ff
3
weh - ren, und al - ler Für - sten höch - stem
mand me, Nor an - y prince that rules on
p
cresc.
ff
fp
Rath!
earth!
Nicht darf sie Zwei - fels Last be -
None shall con - strain or rep - ri -
f
più f
ff Wind.
schweren, sie sa - - - hen mei - ne gu - te
mand me, They saw my deed and know my
Tpts.
f Str.
f
That!
worth!
Nur Ei - ne ist's, der
There's one a - lone, she
Str.
ff
dim.
p Wind.
più p

 (Lohengrin checks himself, seeing with dismay, as he turns towards Elsa, that her bosom is heaving convulsively and her eyes fixed in wild inward commotion.)

Moderato.
muss ich Ant-wort ge-ben: El - sa. El - sa!
can to speak com-pel me! El - sa. El - sa!
Wind.
'Cello.
Trombs.
K. Dr.
wie seh' ich sie er-be-ben!
why thus disturb'd and trembling?
Cor. ingl.
B. Cl.
dim.
Ortrud.
In wil -
By dark
Frederick.
In
By
The King.
Welch ein Ge-heim - niss muss
What-e'er his se - cret, let
The Ladies and Pages.
Welch ein Ge-
What-e'er his
The Men.
Welch ein Ge-heim-niss muss der Held be-wah - ren?
What-e'er his se - cret, he shall not con-fide it.
Welch ein Ge-heim - niss
What-e'er his se - cret,
Tutti.
Fl.

mf
-dem Brü - ten darf ich sie gewah - ren; der Zwei-fel
— sur-mise — I see her heart di-vid - ed, and deep — with-
Lohengrin.
p
In wil - dem
By dark sur -
wil - dem Brü - ten darf — ich sie ge-wah - ren; der
dark sur-mise — I see — her heart di-vid - ed, and
— der Held be-wah - ren? Welch —
— him not con-fide it, what -
p
piu p
Welch ein Ge-heim - niss muss der Held be-wah -
What - e'er his se - cret, he shall not con-fide
piu p
heim - niss muss wohl der Held be-wah -
se - cret, he shall not now con-fide
p
muss der Held be-wah - ren?
he shall not con-fide — it!
Cor. ingl.
p
pp
p
Ped.
Ped.

keimt in ih-res Her - zens Grund.
in her lurks a brood - ing doubt.
Brü - ten muss ich sie ge-wah-ren!
mise I see her heart di-vid-ed!
Zwei - fel keimt in ih-res Her - zens Grund.
deep with - in her lurks a brood - ing doubt.
ein Ge-heim - - -niss? Bringt es ihm
e'er his se - - -cret, let it be
ren?
it!
ren?
it!
p
Bringt es ihm Noth,
Let it be hid,
p
pp
Ped.
*

Der Zwei - fel keimt tief in ih - res
And deep with - in lurk - eth man-y a
Hat sie bethört des Has - ses Lü - -
Have my re - vil - ers tempt - ed her
Der Zwei - fel keimt tief in ih - res
And deep with-in lurk - eth man - y a
Noth, so wahr' es
hid, we trust him
Ver - schweig' es
We trust him
SOPRANO I.
p
Wahr' es
We trust
dim.
so wahr' es treu sein Mund, so wahr' es
we trust him past all doubt, we trust him
Bringt es ihm Noth, so
Let it be hid, we
più p

Elsa. (gazing before her, heedless of the others.)
Was er ver-birgt, wohl brächt' es ihm Ge-fah-ren, vor al-ler
It is not here our fate must be de-cid-ed, be-fore them
Her - zens Grund.
brood - ing doubt.
- gen-mund?
to doubt?
Her - zens Grund.
brood - ing doubt.
treu sein Mund!
past all doubt!
Bringt
Let
treu sein Mund! Bringt sein Ge - heim - niss ihr
past all doubt! Oh, let his se - cret be
SOPRANO II. Bringt sein Ge - heim - niss ihm
Oh, let his se - cret be
treu sein Mund! Bringt sein Ge - heim - niss Noth,
past all doubt! Oh, be his se - cret hid,
treu sein Mund!
past all doubt!
wahr' es sein Mund!
trust past all doubt!
pp Wind.

Welt spräch' es hier aus sein Mund; die er er-
all: that were with dan-ger fraught; oh heart un-
In wil-dem Brü - - ten
By dark sur-mise I
In wil-dem Brü - - ten
By dark sur-mise I
In wil-dem Brü - - ten
By dark sur-mise I
ihm sein Ge-heim-niss Noth, o
it be for ev-er hid, we
Noth, bringt es Noth,
hid, ev-er hid,
Noth, bringt es ihm Noth,
hid, let it be hid,
bringt sein Ge-heim-niss Noth,
let it be ev-er hid,
Ob.

ret - tet, weh mir Un - dank -
grate - ful, why art thou di -
darf ich sie ge -
see her heart di -
muss ich sie ge -
see her heart di -
darf ich sie ge -
see her heart di -
so be - wahr' es
trust, we trust him
molto cresc.
f
Ped.
Ped.
Ped.

ba - ren! ver - rieth' ich ihn, dass hier es wer - de
vid - ed? why art thou torn with wild dis - may and
wah - - - ren!
vid - - - ed!
wah - - - ren!
vid - - - ed!
wah - - - ren!
vid - - - ed!
treu sein Mund!
past all doubt!
so wahr' es ge - treu sein
we trust him be - yond all

kund! Wüsst' ich sein Loos, wüsst' ich sein
doubt! Oh that I knew, oh that I
Er ist be - siegt, er ist be-
He shall re - ply, he shall re-
O Him - mel! schirm', O schir - me ihr Herz! O schir - me ihr
Oh, shield her, Heav'n! oh, shield her from doubt! By thy light a -
Er ist be-siegt, ja! be-
He shall re-ply, yea! his
Wir schir-men ihn, den Ed - - len, vor Ge - fah -
Knight, true of heart, by Heav - - en hith - er guid -
Mund!
doubt!
Wir schirmen ihn, den Ed-len, vor Ge-fah-ren;
Knight, true of heart, by Heav-en hith-er guid-ed,
Wind.
Hns.

Loos, ich wollt' es treu be-wahren! Im
knew! That he in me con-fid-ed! His
siegt, der mir zur Noth in die-ses
ply, I will not live to be by
Herz vor den Ge-fah-ren! Nie wer-de
lone may she be guid-ed! Nor let sus-
siegt ist die-ser Held, der mir zur Noth in die-ses
se-cret shall be known, I will not live to be by
ren; durch sei-ne That ward uns sein
ed; we know him no-ble by the
Bringt ihm sein Ge-heim-niss
His se-cret be ev-er
durch sei-ne That ward uns sein A-del kund!
we know him no-ble by the deeds he wrought!
durch sei-ne That ward uns sein A-del kund!
we know him no-ble by the deeds he wrought!
cresc.
dim.
Str.

Zwei - - fel doch, im Zwei - - fel
se - - cret dark, his se - - cret
cresc.
Land ge-fah - ren, er ist be -
him de-rid - ed, he shall re -
cresc.
Zwei - - fel, nie wer - de Zwei - fel
pi - - cion, nor let sus - pi - - cion
p
cresc.
Land ge - fah - ren, er ist besiegt, er ist be - siegt, wird ihm die
him de - rid - ed, he shall re-ply, he shall re - ply, and thus be
p
cresc.
A - - del kund, ja, durch sei - ne
deeds he wrought, yes, yes, by the
p
cresc.
Noth, bringt ihm
hid, we trust
p
cresc.
p
Wir schir - men ihn, wir schir - men
We trust in him, we trust in
p
p
poco cresc. - - -

doch er - bebt des Her - - zens Grund!
dark I'd guard with heart de - vout!
siegt, wird ihm die Fra - - ge kund.
ply, he shall be brought to naught.
die - ser Rei - nen kund!
taint that heart de - vout!
Fra - ge kund, wird ihm die Fra - ge kund.
brought to naught, he shall be brought to naught.
That ward uns sein A - - del kund;
deeds he wrought, the deeds he wrought;
sein Ge - heim - - niss Noth,
him be - yond all doubt,
ihn, wir schir - - men ihn, den Ed - len, vor Ge
him, we trust in him, we know that he is
cresc.
più f
Tutti.

Im
His
Er ist be-siegt, wird ihm die Fra - ge
He shall re-ply, he shall be brought to
Nie wer-de Zwei - fel der Rei - nen
Faith - ful in trust, keep that heart de -
Er ist be - siegt, wird ihm von ihr die Fra - ge
He shall re - ply, thro' her he shall be bro'ght to
wir schirmen ihn, den Ed - len, vor Ge -
Knight, true of heart, by Heav - en hith - er
so be - wahr' es treu sein Mund,
yea, we trust be - yond all doubt,
fah - ren,
no - ble,
Tpts.
dim.
p
più p

Zwei - fel doch er - bebt des_ Her - zens Grund!
se - cret I would guard with heart de - vout!
kund.
naught!
kund!
vout!
O_ Him - mel, schirme sie
Oh_ Heav'n, by thee alone
kund.
naught!
Be - siegt ist er,
His se - cret known,
fah - ren!
guid - ed!
Wir schir - men ihn vor Ge-
By Heav'n he was hither
wahr' es treu - lich sein Mund!
let his se - cret be hid!
wahr' es treu sein Mund!
be his se - cret hid!
Wir schirmen ihn vor Ge - fahr! Wir schirmen ihn
We trust in him past all doubt! We trust in him
Wind.
Tnr.
dim.
dim. p
pp
f
p

dim.
p
vor den Ge - fah - ren, nie wer-de Zweifel die - ser Rei - nen kund!
may she be guid - ed, nor let sus-picion taint that heart de - vout!
dim.
p
wird ihm — von ihr die Fra - ge kund, wird ihm von ihr die
he shall — thro' her be brought to naught, he shall thro' her be
dim.
p
fah - ren, durch sei - ne That ward uns sein A - del kund,
guid - ed, we know him no - ble by the deeds he wrought,
p
Wahr' es
Be his
p
dim.
p
pp
vor Ge - fahr, wohl ward uns sein A - del kund!
past all doubt, no - ble were the deeds he wrought!
dim.
p
pp
dim.
p
p Wind.

Wüsst' ich sein Loos, wüsst' ich sein Loos!
Oh that I knew, oh that I knew!
Er ist be-siegt, wird ihm die Fra - ge — kund,
He shall re-ply, he shall be brought to — naught,
O Him - mel, schir - me sie!
Oh shield her, shield — her, Heav'n!
Fra - ge kund, wird ihm die Fra - - ge
brought to naught, he shall be brought to
durch sei - ne That al - lein!
yea, by the deeds he wrought.
treu sein Mund!
se - cret hid!
Wir
We
Vl.
più p
molto cresc.

rit.
Wüsst' ich sein Loos!
Oh that I knew!
wird ihm die Fra - ge kund!
he shall be brought to naught!
rit.
O schirme sie!
Oh shield her, Heav'n!
kund, wird ihm die Fra - ge kund!
naught, through her be brought to naught!
rit.
Durch sei - ne That!
Knight, true of heart!
Mein
Brave
dim.
Wahr' er es treu!
For ev - er hid!
dim.
schir - men ihn, den Ed - - len!
trust in him past all doubt!
dim.
dim.
p Wood.
Tutti.

Allegro.
Held, ent-geg-ne kühn dem Un - ge-treu - en!
knight, put him to shame who dares de - fy thee!
Str.
Du bist zu hehr, um, was er klagt, zu
We know thee true, ne'er shall a doubt come
scheu - en; du bist zu hehr, du bist zu hehr,
nigh thee; we know thee true, ne'er shall a doubt,
um, was er klagt, zu scheu - en!
ne'er shall a doubt come nigh thee!
cresc.

The Saxon Nobles (crowding round Lohengrin.)
1st Chorus.
Wir steh'n zu dir! es soll uns nie ge - reu - en,
We trust in thee! though doubt and dan - ger try thee,
The Brabantian Nobles (crowding round Lohengrin.)
2nd Chorus.
Wir steh'n zu dir! es soll uns nicht ge - reu - en,
We trust in thee! though doubt and dan - ger try thee,
dass wir der Hel - den Preis in dir er - kannt! Reich'
to thee we give the prize of high re - nown! Here,
dass wir den Preis dir er - kannt! Reich' uns die
we give the prize of re - nown! Here, take my
dass wir der Hel - den Preis in dir er -
to thee we give the prize of high re -
reu - en, dass wir der Hel - den Preis dir er -
try thee, to thee we give the prize of re -
cresc.

Euch Hel - - den soll der Glau-be nicht ge-reu - en,
Ye val - - - iant hearts, tho' doubt and dan-ger try me,
Reich' uns die Hand! Wir glau-ben dir in Treu - en, dass
Here, take my hand! No dan-ger shall come nigh thee, we
Hand! Wir glau - ben dir in Treu - en, dass
hand! No dan - ger shall come nigh thee, we
kannt! Reich'uns die Hand! Wir glau-ben dir in
nown! Here, take my hand! No dan-ger shall come
kannt! Reich' uns die Hand! Wir glau - ben dir in
nown! Here, take my hand! No dan - ger shall come
werd' euch mein Nam' und Art auch nie ge-nannt;
ye ne'er shall rue the trust this hour hath shown;
hehr dein Nam', auch wenn er nicht genannt; wir glau - ben
trust thee, tho' thy name be still unknown; no dan - ger
hehr dein Nam', auch wenn er nicht ge - nannt; wir
trust thee, tho' thy name be still un - known; no
Treu - en, dass hehr dein Na - - me,
nigh thee, we know thee no - - ble,
Treu - en,
nigh thee,

euch soll der Glau - - - be nicht ge-reu - en,
brave hearts, tho' doubt and dan - ger try me,
dir in Treu - en, dass hehr dein Nam', auch wenn er
shall be - fall thee, we trust thee, tho' thy name be
glau - ben dir in Treu - en, dass hehr dein Nam', auch
dan - ger shall be - fall thee, we trust thee, tho' thy
Reich'
Here,
wir glau - ben dir in Treu - en!
tho' doubt and dan - ger try thee!
Reich'
Here,
werd' euch mein Nam' und Art auch nie ge-nannt.
ne'er shall ye rue the trust this hour hath shown.
(Frederick approaches close to Elsa, who stands, plunged in thought, apart in the foreground.)
Frederick
(in a low voice, interposing vehemently.)
Vertrau-e mir!
Confide in me!
nicht genannt. Reich' uns die Hand, reich' uns die Hand!
still unknown. Here, take my hand, here, take my hand!
wenn er nicht ge-nannt. Reich' uns die Hand!
name be still un-known. Here, take my hand!
uns die Hand,
take my hand,
Reich' uns die Hand, reich' uns die Hand!
Here, take my hand, here, take my hand!
uns die Hand, reich' uns die Hand!
take my hand, here, take my hand!
cresc.
Wind.
Tnr. & Cello.

(The men form a circle round Lohengrin, and all successively grasp his hand in token of allegiance.)
Elsa (startled, but sotto voce.)
p
Hin-
A-
Lass dir ein Mit - tel hei-ssen, das dir Ge-wiss-heit schafft!
Let me a se-cret tell thee, hear and con-vince thy-self!
Bssn.
cresc.
weg von mir!
way from me!
Lass mich das klein-ste Glied ihm nur ent-rei-ssen, des
Give me but leave the small-est limb to maim him, one
p
Fin-gers Spit-ze, und ich schwö-re dir, was er dir hehlt, sollst frei du vor dir
drop of life-blood, and I swear to thee, what now he hides, he free-ly shall de-
Cor.ingl.
cresc.
p
cresc.
Elsa.
Ha! Nimmermehr!
Ah! tempt me not!
seh'n, dir treu, soll nie er dir von hinnen geh'n!
clare, Nor ev-er from thy side to wander dare!
Ich bin dir nah' zur
This night I shall be
Vl.
più cresc.
fp

Lohengrin (stepping
Nacht, — rufst du, ohn' Scha - den ist es schnell voll-bracht! El - sa, mit
near, Call me, and straight I'll come all doubt to clear! El - sa, with
sf cresc.
ff
hastily forward.)
(In a terrible tone, to Ortrud and Frederick.)
wem verkehrst du da? Zu - rück
whom dost thou con-verse? A - way
mf
cresc.
ff
von ihr, Ver - fluch - te! Dass nie mein Au - ge
from her, ac - curs'd ones! On per - il of my
Wind.
Hns.
(Frederick makes a gesture of pain and rage.)
je euch wie - der bei ihr seh'!
wrath, dare ye to cross her path!
Str.
più f
(Lohengrin turns towards Elsa, who, as he calls her name, sinks overwhelmed at his feet.)
Più moderato.
El - sa, er - he - be dich! In
El - sa, a - rise, my love! In
molto espress.
ff
rit.
dim.
più p

dei-ner Hand, in dei-ner Treu' liegt al-les Glü-ckes Pfand!
thy com-mand, In thy good faith my ev-'ry hope doth stand!
p
più p
pp
f Fl. & Ob.
Lässt nicht des Zwei-fels Macht dich ruh'n? Willst du die
Doth an-y doubt thy heart in-spire? Dost thou to
Cl.
ffp
f
ffp
lento.
Elsa (in a tumult of emotion, shame
Fra-ge an mich thun? Mein Ret-ter, der mir
question me de-sire? My champion, my de-
Ob.
Wind.
ff lento.
dim.
pp
Vl.
and confusion.)
Heil ge-bracht! Mein Held, in dem ich muss ver-geh'n!
liv-'rer dear! Oh thou who dost my soul sus-tain!
(Significantly and with decision.)
Hoch ü-ber al-les Zwei-fels Macht soll mei-ne Lie-be
High o'er the reach of doubt and fear, Love o-ver all shall
dim.
p
Wind.
p
f
dim.
più p
pp

(she sinks upon his breast.)
Lohengrin.
(Lohengrin solemnly conducts Elsa past the nobles, to the King.)
lento.
p
stehn! Heil dir, El - sa! Nun lass vor Gott uns gehn!
reign! Come then, El - sa! come, let us plight our faith!
The Ladies and Pages.
pp
Heil! Heil!
Hail! Hail!
pp
Heil! Heil! Heil!
Hail! Hail! Hail!
(in enthusiastic emotion.)
pp
The Men.
Seht, er ist von Gott ge - sandt!
Lo, he is from Heav - en sent!
pp
lento.
p Org.
Wind.
p
Ped.
(As Lohengrin passes with Elsa, the men deferentially make way.)
The Men.
TENOR I.
TENOR II.
p
Heil El - sa von Bra -
Hail, El - sa of Bra -
BASS I.
BASS II.
p
Heil, Heil euch!
Hail, blest pair!
Ped.

(Conducted by the King, Lohengrin and Elsa slowly approach the Minster.)

cresc.
dir, Tu-gend-rei-che, Heil El-sa von Bra-bant! Heil
thou roy-al maid-en, Hail, El-sa of Bra-bant! Hail,
più cresc.
Tu-gend-rei-che! Heil dir! Heil
roy-al maid-en! Hail, oh! Hail,
Heil! Heil
Hail! Hail,
lei-ten, ge-segnet sollst du schrei-ten! Heil dir, Tu-gend-
lad-en, go forth, with bless-ings lad-en! Hail, thou roy-al
più f
più cresc.
molto cresc.
dir! Heil dir, Heil El-
oh hail, roy-al El-
rei-che, Heil, Heil dir, Heil El-
maid-en, oh hail, roy-al El-

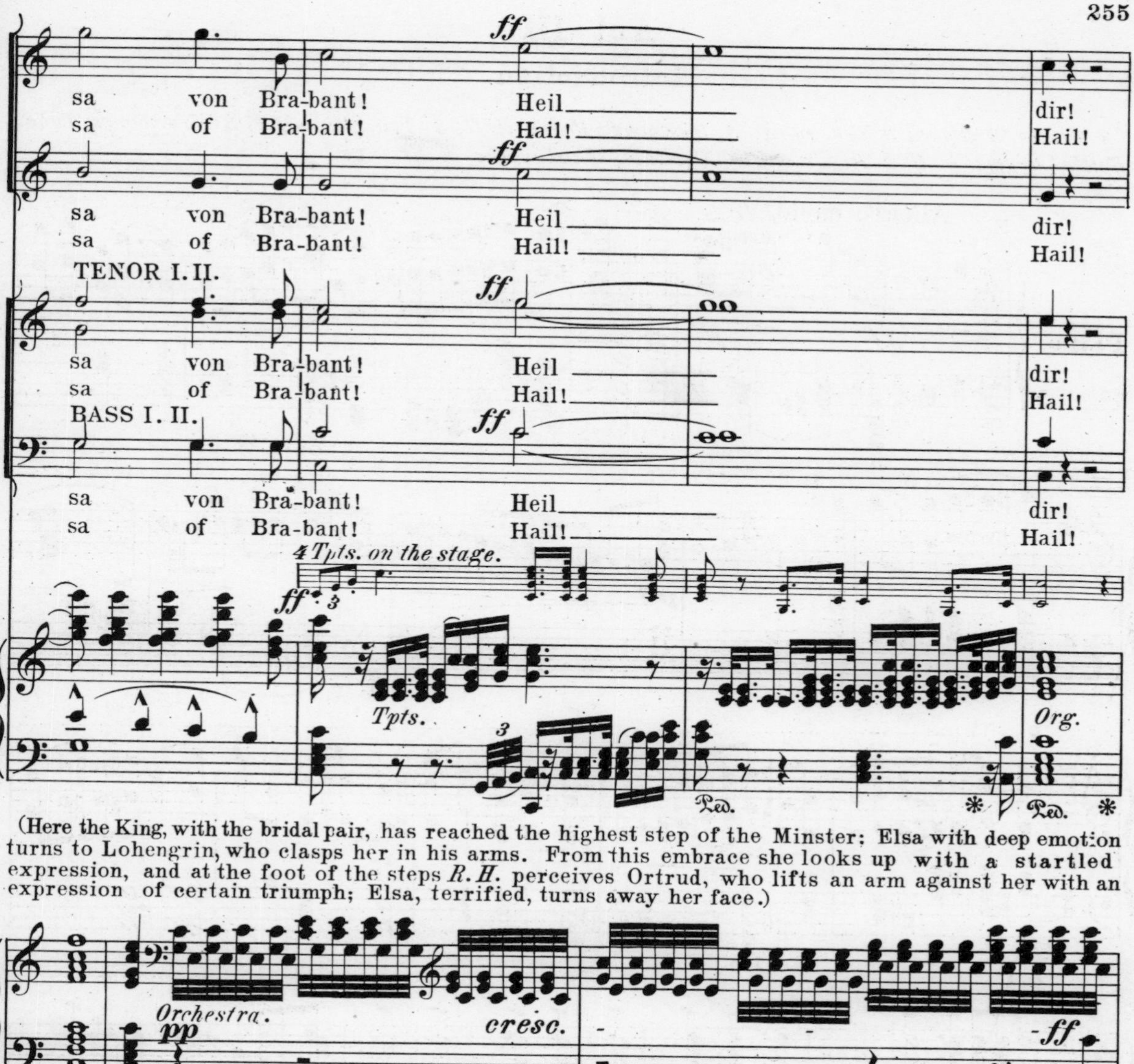

sa von Bra-bant! Heil ——— dir!
sa of Bra-bant! Hail! ——— Hail!

sa von Bra-bant! Heil ——— dir!
sa of Bra-bant! Hail! ——— Hail!

TENOR I. II.

sa von Bra-bant! Heil ——— dir!
sa of Bra-bant! Hail! ——— Hail!

BASS I. II.

sa von Bra-bant! Heil ——— dir!
sa of Bra-bant! Hail! ——— Hail!

4 *Tpts. on the stage.*

ff *Tpts.* *Org.*

(Here the King, with the bridal pair, has reached the highest step of the Minster; Elsa with deep emotion turns to Lohengrin, who clasps her in his arms. From this embrace she looks up with a startled expression, and at the foot of the steps R. H. perceives Ortrud, who lifts an arm against her with an expression of certain triumph; Elsa, terrified, turns away her face.)

(As Elsa and Lohengrin, conducted by the King,

proceed to the entrance of the Minster, the curtain falls.)

End of the Second Act.

Act III.

Introduction.

3 Flutes, 3 Oboes, 3 Cls. in A, 3 Bassoons, Horns in G, 3 Trumpets in C, 3 Trombones, Tuba, Kettle-drums in G & D, Triangle, Cymbals, Tambourine & Strings.

8
Vl. Fl. Ob. & Cl.
sempre ff
ff
3
'Cello, Bssn. Hns. & Trombs.
8
3
3
8
8
ff
tr
8
Ped.
3
3
Wind
mf
dim.
p
p

mf dim.
p
mf dim.
p
mf dim.
p
Cl.
molto cresc.
f
p
Cl.
cresc.
f
dim.
riten.
a tempo
p dolce
ff
tr
ff
D. Bass Trombs.
Hns. & Bssn.

(The curtain rises.)

Scene I.

(The bridal chamber; to the right, an oriel casement, which is open. Music behind the stage, at first heard quite in the distance, and gradually approaching nearer; at the middle of the strain, doors at the back of the stage *R.* and *L.* are opened; the Ladies enter *R. H.* leading in Elsa, the King and Nobles leading in Lohengrin; Pages with lights go before them.)

On the stage. *3 Flutes, 2 Oboes, 2 Cls. in B, 2 Bassoons, Horns in B flat & E flat, 2 Trumpets in B flat, Triangle & Harp.*
In the Orchestra. (*Same score except Triangle, Cymbals & Tambourine, with Harp added.*)

eint euch in Treu - e zum se - lig - sten Paar.
Blest be ye both far from all life's an - noy.
TENOR I.
Strei - ter der
Cham - pion vic -
Tu - gend, schrei - te vor - an!
to - rious, go thou be - fore!
TENOR I & II.
TENOR I.
Zier - de der Ju - gend,
Maid bright and glo - rious,
schrei - te vor - an!
go thou be - fore!
Rau - schen des Fe - stes
Mirth's nois - y rev - el
Dem Fe - - - - ste
The rev - - - - el

seid nun ent - ron - nen,
ye have for - sak - en,
seid ent - ron - nen, Won - ne des Her - zens
ye've for - sak - en, Ten - der de - lights for
seid nun ent - ron - nen, Won - ne des Her - zens
ye have for - sak - en, Ten - der de - lights for
seid ent - ron - nen, Won - ne des Her - zens
ye've for - sak - en, Ten - der de - lights for
(Here the doors are opened.)
p
sei euch ge - won - nen! Duf - ten - der Raum, zur Lie - be ge -
you now a - wak - en! Fra - grant a - bode en - shrine ye in
sei euch ge - won - nen! Duf - ten - der Raum, zur Lie - be ge -
you now a - wak - en! Fra - grant a - bode en - shrine ye in
sei euch ge - won - nen! Duf - ten - der Raum, zur Lie - be ge -
you now a - wak - en! Fra - grant a - bode en - shrine ye in
dim.
schmückt, nehm' euch nun auf, dem Glan - ze ent - rückt.
bliss, Splen - dor and state in joy ye dis - miss.
schmückt, nehm' euch nun auf, dem Glan - ze ent - rückt.
bliss, Splen - dor and state in joy ye dis - miss.
schmückt, nehm' euch nun auf, dem Glan - ze ent - rückt.
bliss, Splen - dor and state in joy ye dis - miss.

p
Treu-lich ge- führt zie-het nun ein, wo euch der
Faith-ful and true, we lead ye forth, Where love tri-
p
Treu-lich ge- führt zie-het nun ein, wo euch der
Faith-ful and true, we lead ye forth, Where love tri-
p
Treu-lich ge- führt zie-het nun ein, wo euch die
Faith-ful and true, we lead ye forth, Where love shall
p Wind in Orchestra.
Se-gen der Lie-be be- wahr'! Sieg-rei-cher Muth,
um-phant shall crown ye with joy. Star of re- nown,
Se-gen der Lie-be be- wahr'! Sieg-rei-cher Muth,
um-phant shall crown ye with joy. Star of re- nown,
Lie- - be be- wahr'! Sieg-rei-cher Muth,
crown ye with joy. Star of re- nown,
mf
Min- ne so rein eint euch in Treu- e zum
flow'r of the earth, Blest be ye both, far from
cresc.
Min- ne so rein eint euch in Treu- e zum
flow'r of the earth, Blest be ye both, far from
cresc.
Min- ne so rein eint euch in Treu- e zum
flow'r of the earth, Blest be ye both, far from
cresc.

dim.
se - lig - sten Paar, zum se - lig - sten Paar!
all life's an - noy, from all life's an - noy!
dim.
se - lig - sten Paar. In Treu - e!
all life's an - noy, Be hap - py!
dim.
se - lig - sten Paar. In Treu - e!
all life's an - noy, Be hap - py!
Wind.
Str.
Eight Ladies. (after they have gone round once.)
FOUR SOPRANOS.
(When the two trains meet in the centre of the stage, the Ladies lead Elsa to Lohengrin, who embrace, and remain thus standing in the centre. Eight Ladies walk in slow procession round Lohengrin and Elsa, while these are divested of their heavy upper garments by the Pages.)
Wie Gott euch
As sol - emn
FOUR ALTOS.
poco più lento.
Str. pizz.
se - lig weih - te, zu Freu - den weih'n euch wir;
vows u - nite ye, We hal - low ye to joy!

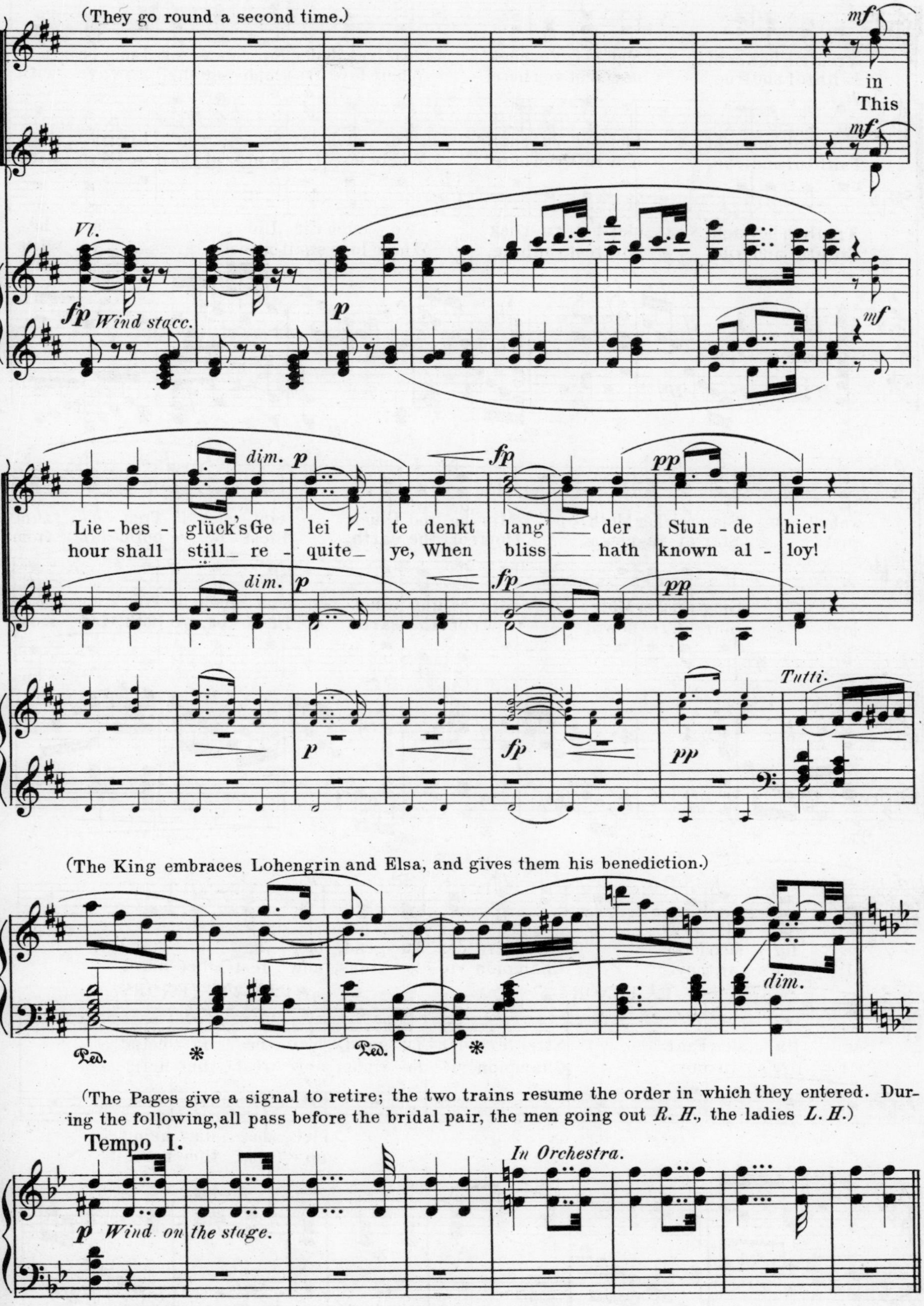

(They go round a second time.)

mf

in
This

mf

Vl.

fp *Wind stacc.*

p

mf

dim. *p* *fp* *pp*

Lie - bes - glück's Ge - lei - te denkt lang der Stun - de hier!
hour shall still re - quite ye, When bliss hath known al - loy!

dim. *p* *fp* *pp*

p *fp* *pp*

Tutti.

(The King embraces Lohengrin and Elsa, and gives them his benediction.)

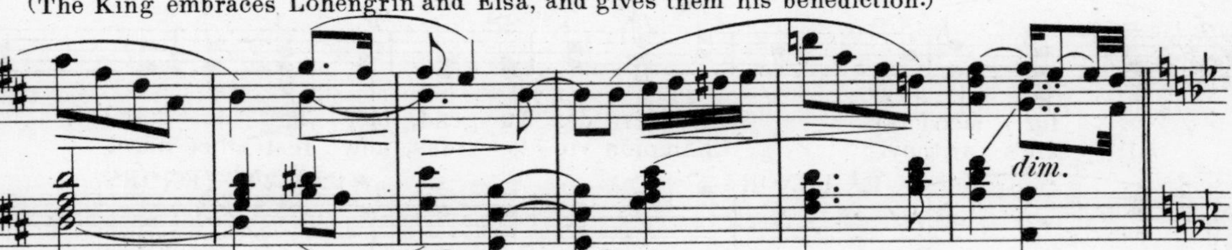

(The Pages give a signal to retire; the two trains resume the order in which they entered. During the following, all pass before the bridal pair, the men going out *R. H.*, the ladies *L. H.*)

Tempo I.

All the Nobles and Ladies.
Treulich bewacht blei-bet zu-rück, wo euch der Se-gen der Lie-be be-
Faithful and true, now rest you here, Where love tri-umph-ant shall crown ye with
Treulich bewacht blei-bet zu-rück, wo euch der Se-gen der Lie-be be-
Faithful and true, now rest you here, Where love tri-umph-ant shall crown ye with
Treulich bewacht blei-bet zu-rück, wo euch die Lie-be be-
Faithful and true, now rest you here, Where love shall crown ye with
Hp. & Wind.
wahr'! Sieg-reicher Muth, Min-ne und Glück eint euch in Treu-e zum
joy! Star of re-nown, flow'r of the earth, Blest be ye both, far from
wahr'! Sieg-reicher Muth, Min-ne und Glück eint euch in Treu-e zum
joy! Star of re-nown, flow'r of the earth, Blest be ye both, far from
se-lig-sten Paar. Strei-ter der Tu-gend, blei-be da-heim!
all life's an-noy. Champion vic-to-rious, now rest thee here!
1st TENOR. 1st & 2nd TENORS.
se-lig-sten Paar. Strei-ter der Tu-gend, blei-be da-heim!
all life's an-noy. Champion vic-to-rious, now rest thee here!
blei-be da-heim!
now rest thee here!

p Zier - de der Ju - gend, *p* blei - be da - heim! Rau - schen des
Maid bright and glo - rious, now rest thee here! Mirth's nois - y

TENOR I. *p* **TENOR I & II.** *p*

Zier - de der Ju - gend, blei - be da - heim! Rau - schen des
Maid bright and glo - rious, now rest thee here! Mirth's nois - y

p
blei - be da - heim! Dem Fe -
now rest thee here! The rev -

Str.

Ped. *

seid — nun ent - ron - nen,
ye — have for - sak - en,

Fe - stes seid ent - ron - nen, Won - ne des Her - zens
rev - el ye've for - sak - en, Ten - der de - lights for

Fe - stes seid nun ent - ron - nen, Won - ne des Her - zens
rev - el ye have for - sak - en, Ten - der de - lights for

- ste seid ent - ron - nen, Won - ne des Her - zens
- el ye've for - sak - en, Ten - der de - lights for

sei euch ge - won - nen! *p* Duf - ten - der Raum, zur Lie - be ge - schmückt,
you now a - wak - en! Fra - grant a - bode en - shrine ye in bliss,

p
sei euch ge - won - nen! Duf - ten - der Raum, zur Lie - be ge - schmückt,
you now a - wak - en! Fra - grant a - bode en - shrine ye in bliss,

p
sei euch ge - won - nen! Duf - ten - der Raum, zur Lie - be ge - schmückt,
you now a - wak - en! Fra - grant a - bode en - shrine ye in bliss,

Wind.

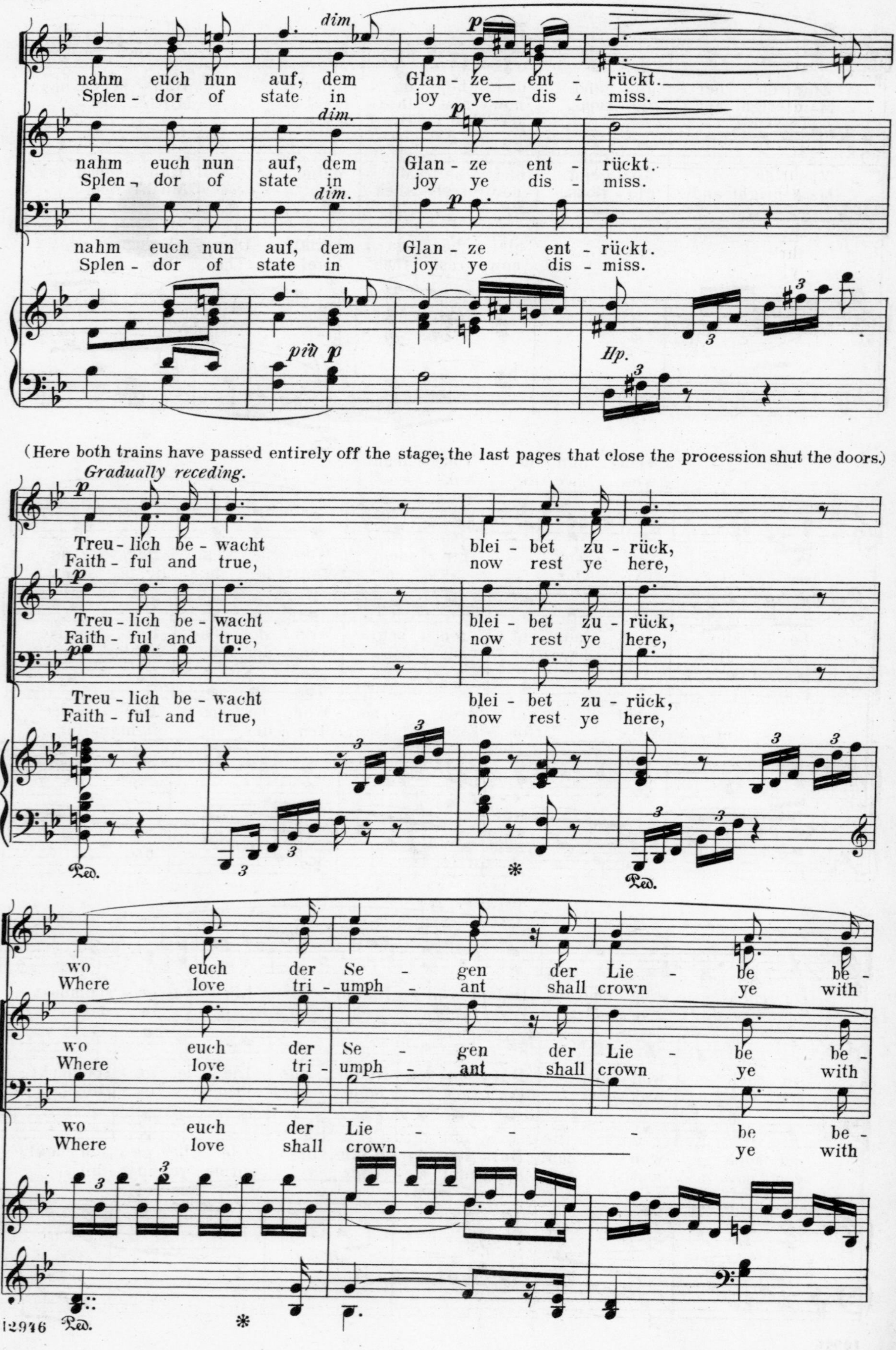

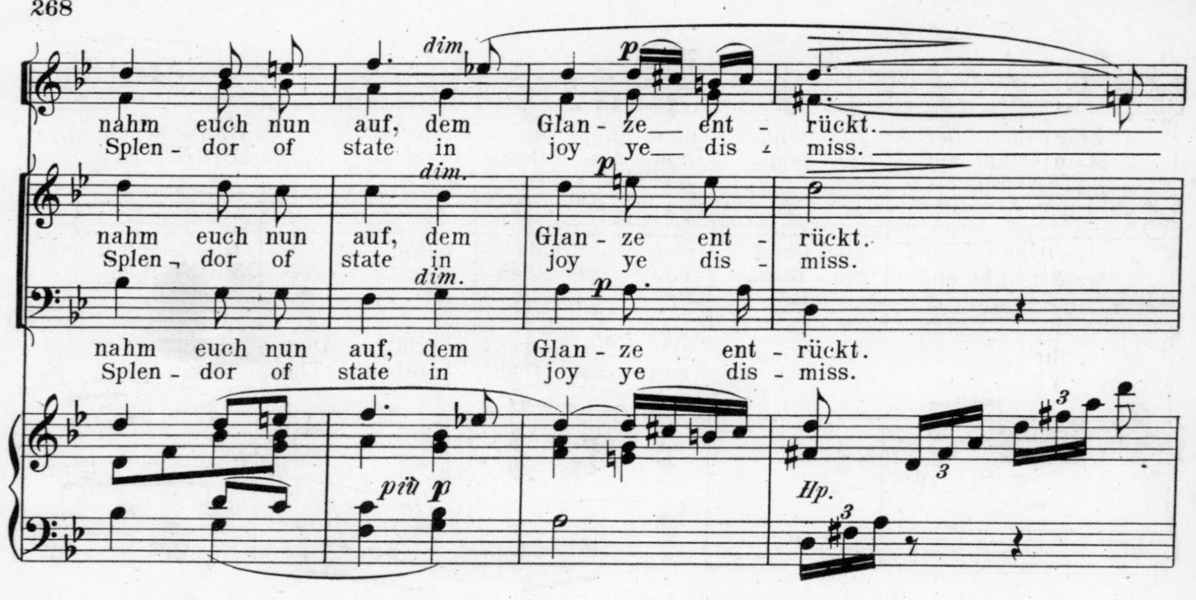

dim
p
nahm euch nun auf, dem Glan-ze ent-rückt.
Splen-dor of state in joy ye dis-miss.
dim.
p
nahm euch nun auf, dem Glan-ze ent-rückt.
Splen-dor of state in joy ye dis-miss.
dim.
p
nahm euch nun auf, dem Glan-ze ent-rückt.
Splen-dor of state in joy ye dis-miss.
più p
Hp.
(Here both trains have passed entirely off the stage; the last pages that close the procession shut the doors.)
Gradually receding.
p
Treu-lich be-wacht blei-bet zu-rück,
Faith-ful and true, now rest ye here,
p
Treu-lich be-wacht blei-bet zu-rück,
Faith-ful and true, now rest ye here,
p
Treu-lich be-wacht blei-bet zu-rück,
Faith-ful and true, now rest ye here,
Ped.
*
Ped.
wo euch der Se-gen der Lie-be be-
Where love tri-umph-ant shall crown ye with
wo euch der Se-gen der Lie-be be-
Where love tri-umph-ant shall crown ye with
wo euch der Lie-be be-
Where love shall crown ye with
Ped.
*

wahr'! Sieg - rei - cher Muth, Min - ne und
joy! Star of re - nown, flow'r of the

wahr'! Sieg - rei - cher Muth, Min - ne und
joy! Star of re - nown, flow'r of the

wahr'! Sieg - rei - cher Muth, Min - ne und
joy! Star of re - nown, flow'r of the

Glück eint euch in Treu - e zum se - - - -
earth, Blest be ye both far from all

Glück eint euch in Treu - e zum se - - - -
earth, Blest be ye both far from all

Glück eint euch in Treu - e zum se - - - -
earth, Blest be ye both far from all

(When the procession has quitted the room, Elsa, overcome by emotion, sinks upon Lohengrin's breast. As the music dies away he seats himself on a couch by the oriel window, and draws Elsa gently towards him.)

(dying away.)

- lig-sten Paar, zum se - lig - sten Paar!
life's an - noy, from all life's an - noy!

- lig-sten Paar. In Treu - e!
life's an - noy. Here rest ye!

lig - sten Paar.
life's an - noy,

Da lontano

pp Str. con Sord.

Second Scene.

(Elsa and Lohengrin.)

(Same score as before, except Harp)

Elsa.
Wie wär' ich kalt, mich glücklich nur zu nennen, be-sitz' ich al-ler
Words can-not tell the rapt-ure sweet and ten-der That floods my soul with
traut!
life?
Str.
fp
dim.
Un poco più lento.
p
Him-mel Se-lig-keit! Fühl' ich zu dir so süss mein Herz entbrennen,
joy, with joy di-vine! When thou dost bend o'er me thy glance of splendor,
Wood.
f dim. più p
pp Str
ath-me ich Won-nen, die nur Gott ver-leiht, fühl' ich zu dir so
When thou art near, the bliss of heav'n is mine, words can-not tell this
p
Lohen-
pp mf mf
süss mich entbren-nen, ath-me ich Won-nen, die nur Gott ver-leiht! Ver-
joy sweet and ten-der, when thou art near, the bliss of heav'n is mine! Thy
pp dim.
grin. (ardently.)
magst du, Hol-de! glück-lich dich zu nen-nen, giebst du auch mir des
words, oh fair-est, well thy transports ren-der, If thou art blest, thy
mf dim. p mf
Ped. *

(tenderly.)
Himmels Se-lig- keit! Fühl' ich zu dir so süss mein Herz entbrennen,
joy is doub-ly mine! Bend thou on me those eyes so soft and ten-der,
Ob.
Vl.
fp
pp
Wood.
Str.
Elsa.
Fühl' ich so
I feel a
ath-me ich Won-nen, die nur Gott ver-leiht; fühl' ich so süss,
Oh let me breathe with thee a joy di-vine, bend thou on me,
Fl. & Cl.
süss mich ent-bren-nen, so süss mich ent-bren-nen,
joy sweet and ten-der, a joy sweet and ten-der,
fühl' ich so süss mich ent-bren-nen,
oh bend those eyes soft and ten-der,
p Wood.
mf Str.
pp Wood.
ath- - me ich Won- nen, die nur
oh, let me breathe with thee this
ath- - me ich Won- nen, die nur
oh, let me breathe with thee this
Str. molto cresc.
dim.
ff

dim. p
più p
Poco più animato.
Gott ver-leiht, die nur Gott ver - leiht!
joy di-vine, breathe this joy di - vine!
Gott ver - leiht, die nur Gott ver - leiht!
joy di - vine, breathe this joy di - vine!
Poco più animato.
Fl.
pp
Lohengrin.
Wie hehr er-kenn' ich un-srer Lie-be
With charm-ed links did Heav'n to thee u-
Cl.
Vl.
dim.
più p
We-sen! Die nie sich sah'n, wir hat-ten uns ge-ahnt; war
nite me! Ere yet we met, thy heart had dreams of me, And
cresc.
mf
ich zu deinem Streiter aus-er-le-sen, hat Lie-be mir zu dir den Weg ge-
if as champion I was call'd to right thee, 'Twas love a-lone that led my way to

mf
dim.
p
riten.
bahnt: dein Au - ge sag - te mir dich rein von Schuld, mich zwang dein Blick zu
thee. I knew_thee pure from ev'ry taint of wrong, To thee my heart and
più p
fp
Elsa.
dienen dei - ner Huld. Doch ich zu - vor schon hat - te dich ge - sehen,
homage true be - long. I saw thee first from azure heights descending,
riten.
p
Wood. dim.
p
pp
p
in sel - 'gem Trau - me warst du mir ge - naht;
'Twas in a dream thy form I first be - held;
Str.
p
Fl. & Cl.
als ich nun wachend dich sah vor mir ste - hen,
When o'er my wak-ing eyes I saw thee bend - ing,
poco cresc.
lento.
Animato.
er - kannt' ich, dass du kamst auf Go - tes Rath. Da wollte
I knew thee sent as an - gels were of old. My heart with
Str.
Cl & Bssn.
f
p
pp
più p
fp

ich vor dei-nem Blick zer-flie-ssen, gleich ei-nem Bach um-win-den dei-nen
joy would fain dis-solve be-fore thee, I'd trace thy steps as brook thro' flow'ry
Schritt, als ei-ne Blu-me, duftend auf der Wie-sen, wollt' ich ent-
mead, Like od'rous ros-es, sweetness I'd waft o'er thee, Dy-ing for
cresc.
ritard.
Più lento.
animandosi
zückt mich beugen deinem Tritt. Ist dies nur Lie-be? — Wie soll ich es
thy dear sake were blest in-deed! Say, do I love thee? By what blissful
più p
Wood.
dim.
Str.
accel.
più lento
dim.
nen-nen, dies Wort, so un-aus-sprechlich wonne-voll, wie, ach! dein Na-me, den ich
to-ken Is shown that pow'r so dread and yet so blest? Or like thy name, ah, may it
Wood.
dim.
Lohengrin.
(caressingly.)
nie darf ken-nen, bei dem ich nie mein Höch-stes nen-nen soll! El-sa!
not be spok-en? Must what I prize the most be ne'er ex-press'd? El-sa!
Str.
cresc.

Elsa.
(lingering over her words.)
Wie süss mein Na-me deinem Mund' ent-gleitet! Gönnst du des dei-nen holden Klang mir
How sweet my name, as from thy lips it glided! Canst thou de-ny to me the sound of
nicht? Nur, wenn zur Lie-bes-stil-le wir ge-lei-tet, sollst du ge-
thine? In bliss-ful hour thou'lt to my heart con-fide it, That of thy
stat-ten, dass mein Mund ihn spricht. Ein-sam, wenn Niemand wacht; nie sei der
love shall be the seal and sign! Soft-ly, when none are nigh, Whis-per the
Lohengrin.
Mein süsses Weib!
Oh, my sweet wife!
Moderato mosso.
Welt er zu Ge-hör ge-bracht!
word, none e'er shall hear but I.
(Lohengrin tenderly embraces Elsa, and points through the open casement to the flower-garden.)
Wood.
Lohengrin.
Ath-mest du nicht mit mir die sü-ssen Düf-te?
Say, dost thou breathe the in-cense sweet of flow-ers?
Str. con sordini.
simile.
Cello.
dim.
più p
pp
mf
p

O_wie so hold be-rau-schen sie den Sinn! Ge-heim-niss-voll sie
Bearing a tide of deep, mys-te-rious joy! And wouldst thou know from
sempre pp
na-hen durch die Lüf-te,_ frag-los___ geb' ih-rem Zau- - ber ich mich
whence this rapture showers? Ask not-___ lest thou the won- - drous charm de-
(raising his voice.)
hin. So ist der Zauber, der mich dir ver-bun-den, da als ich zu-
stroy. Such is the magic that to thee hath bound me, When I first be-
Wind.
p
mf
erst, du Süs-se, dich er-sah; nicht dei-ne Art ich
held thy beau-ty past com-pare; Know-ing thee not, I
dim.
più p
mf
dimin.
brauch-te zu er-kun-den, dich sah mein Aug',_ mein Herz be-griff dich
worshipp'd and re-nown'd thee, I felt thy glance, and knew thee true as
p
f
p
Ped.
*

da. Wie mir die Düf - te hold den Sinn be -
fair. And as the o - d'rous gales with rap-ture
Str.
p
pp
Fl.
Fl.
Ped.
*
rü - cken, nah'n sie mir gleich aus räth - sel-vol-ler
fire me, Borne on the dark, un - fath - om'd gloom of
(with ardor)
Nacht, so dei - ne Rei - ne muss - te mich ent -
night, Thus thou to trust un - meas - ur'd didst in -
cresc.
fp
zü - cken, traf ich dich auch in
spire me, When thou wert crush'd by
p
mf
p
più p
lento.
(Elsa conceals her confusion by clinging devotedly to Lohengrin.)
schwerer Schuld Ver - dacht.
dark sus-pic - ion's blight.
lento.
pp
Fl. & Cl.
p
Ped.
*

Elsa.

Ach! könnt' ich dei-ner werth er-schei-nen! Müsst' ich vor
Ah! could I show my deep de-vo-tion, Do some good

tranquillo. *p* Str. *simile.*

dir nicht — bloss ver-geh'n! Könnt' ein Verdienst mich dir ver-
deed, wor-thy of thee! Naught have I but my fond e-

ei-nen, dürft' ich in Pein für dich mich seh'n! Wie
mo-tion, Nev-er can I thy e-qual be! Were

p

du mich traf'st vor schwe-rer Kla-ge, o! wüss-te ich auch dich in
doubt and dan-ger lowr'-ing o'er thee, As once they threaten'd me with

p *f*

Noth! Dass muth-voll ich ein Mü-hen
woe, And I could to thy right re-

mf *p*

dim.
p
p
tra - ge, kennt' ich ein Sor - gen, das dir droht! Wär' das Ge-
store thee, Then might my heart some comfort know! Hap - ly thy
Ob.
dim.
più p pp
ff
p dim.
(with growing mystery.
heimniss so ge - ar - tet, das al - ler Welt verschweigt dein Mund? Vielleicht, dass
secret's fraught with danger, There-fore thy lips to all are clos'd! 'T shall ne'er be
Wind.
Vl.
Wind.
Vl.
p
più p
Un-heil dich er - war - tet, würd' al - ler Welt es of - fen kund?
known to friend or stranger, If thou in me thy trust re - pose.
Wind.
Vl.
Wind.
Str.
pp
p cresc.
Wär' es so! und dürft' ich's wissen, dürft' ich in meiner Macht es sehn, durch
Doubt me not, oh let me share it, Oh, let me know thy faith complete! Not
Wind.
Str.
fp
fp
p cresc.
Kei - nes Droh'n sei mir's ent - rissen, für dich wollt' ich zum To - de
death it - self from me shall tear it, And tor - ture borne for thee were
f
p cresc.
f

Lohengrin.
Elsa (more and more impetuously.)
geh'n! Ge-lieb - te! O mach'mich stolz durch dein Ver-
sweet! My lov'd one! O make me glad with thy re-
p cresc.
fp
mfp
trau - en, dass ich in Un-werth nicht ver-geh'! Lass dein Ge-
li - ance, Hum - ble me not, that bend so low! Ne'er shalt thou
p
cresc.
slowly.
heim - niss mich er-schau - en, dass, wer du bist, ich of-fen
rue thy dear af - fi - ance, Him that I love, oh let me
fp
riten.
fp
Lohengrin.
Elsa (more and more urgently.)
seh'! Ach,schweige,Elsa! Mei - ner Treu - e ent-hül-le dei-nes A-dels
know! No more, oh Elsa! Tell, oh tell me,Reveal thy name ador'd to
f
ff
mf
p
Werth! Wo-her du kamst, sag' oh-ne Reu - e, durch
love! Thy race and name, all that be-fell thee, My
cresc.

Slower.
Lohengrin (sternly and gravely, stepping back a few paces.)
mich sei Schweigens Kraft be-währt!
pow'r of si - lence thou shalt prove!
Höch-stes Vertrau'n hast du mir schon zu dan-ken, da deinem Schwur ich Glau-ben gern gewährt;
Great-est of trusts, oh El-sa, I have shewn thee, When I be-lieved thee true from ev-'ry stain,
Trombs.
dim.
Str.
Tnr.,'Cello & Trombs.
più
cresc.
wirst nimmer du vor dem Ge - bo-te wanken, hoch ü-ber al-le Frau'n dünkst du mich werth!
Wav'ring in faith, if thou shouldst ev-er own thee, Thy empire o'er my heart thou'lt ne'er re - gain.
(He quickly turns again fondly towards Elsa.)
Molto più vivo.
Vl.
An meine Brust, du Sü-sse, Rei-ne!
Oh let my arms in love en-fold thee!
Wind.

Sei mei-nes Herzens Glü-hen nah, dass mich dein Au-ge sanft be-
Come, rest thee here, my love, my life, Let me in ra-diant joy be-
Wind
Str.
scheine, in dem ich all' mein Glück er-sah!
hold thee, Far from our hearts be thought of strife!
(ardently.)
O, gönne mir, dass mit Ent-
Come, to my heart oh let me
Vl.
zü-cken ich dei-nen A-them sau-ge ein!
press thee, Let me in-hale thy o-d'rous breath!
Lass fest, ach! fest an mich dich
An-gels might glo-ry to pos-
riten.
drü-cken, dass ich in dir mög' glück-lich sein!
sess thee, Oh turn to me in lov-ing faith!
molto tranquillo
Tpt.
1st Vl.
più p
Dein Lie-ben muss mir hoch ent-gel-ten für
Thy love a-lone for all con-soles me, That
2nd Vl. Tns. & Cello pizz.

das, was ich um dich ver- liess;
I for thy dear sake have lost;
sempre pp
Wind.
Ped.
kein Loos in Got-tes wei- - - ten-
A high and glo-rious fate con-
Wel - ten wohl ed - ler als das mei - - ne
trols me, The fate true knights must prize the
hiess'! Böt' mir der
most! As when the
fp Wind.
Kö-nig sei-ne Kro - - ne, ich dürf-te sie mit Recht ver-
King desir'd to crown me, My heart dis-dain'd the prof-fer'd
fp
f p Tpts.
Str.
mf p

poco più lento.

schmäh'n: das Ein-z'ge, was mein Opfer loh - ne, das
boon, No earth-ly glo-ry can re-nown me, no

f *dim.* *p*

come prima, ma ritardando un poco.

sempre rit.

Ein-z'ge, was mein Op-fer loh-ne, muss ich in dei-ner Lieb er-seh'n! Drum wolle
earth-ly glo-ry can re-nown me, I glo-ry in thy love a-lone! Let not a

fp *p* *più p* *pp* B. Cl.

stets den Zwei-fel meiden, dein Lie - ben sei mein stolz Ge-
doubt thy spir-it bor-row, Thy love ___ is all the world to

Ob. & Cl. *fp* Wind. Str. *f* Tpts.

währ; denn nicht komm' ich aus Nacht und Lei-den, aus
me, I came not here from night and sor-row, From

p *fp*

lento. Allegro molto.

Elsa.

Glanz und Won-ne komm' ich her! Hilf Gott, was muss ich hö-ren! Welch'
blest de-light I came to thee. Help, Heav'n! What dost thou tell me! What

Vl. con passione. *fp* *f* *p* Wind.

Zeug-niss gab dein Mund! Du woll-test mich be - thö - ren, nun
must thy lips re - late! With glam-or thou'dst be - guile me, I
cresc.
sempre
wird mir Jam - mer kund!
know my wretch - ed fate!
cresc.
più f
Das Loos, dem du ent - ron - nen, es
The lot thou hast for - sak - en, Is
ff
fp
Cello.
p
war dein höch-stes Glück: du kamst zu mir aus Won - nen, und
still thy heart's de-sire; One day I shall a - wak - en When
fp
cresc.
seh-nest dich zu - rück! Wie soll ich Aerm-ste glau - ben, dir
thou of me shalt tire! Oh how can I be - lieve thee, I
f
p
cresc.

più lento.
g'nü - ge mei - ne Treu? Ein Tag wird dich mir rau - ben durch
know that we must part! Of joy thy words be - reave_me, Hope
Wind.
colla parte.
Str.
a tempo. Allegro.
dei - ner Lie - be Reu, durch dei - ner Lie - be
fades with - in my heart, hope fades with - in my
Lohengrin.
Halt'
No
Reu! Was quä - lest du mich doch? Soll ich die
heart! On thee I yet may gaze! Un - til de -
ein, dich so zu qua - len!
more, oh I be - seech thee!
Ta - ge zäh - len, die du mir blei - best noch? In Sorg' um dein Ver -
spair shall reach me, Oh, must I count the days? In dread my soul shall
wei - len ver - blüht die Wan - ge mir; dann wirst du mir ent - ei - len, im E -
lan - guish, Lest from my sight thou fly; Thou'lt leave me in my an - guish, Of sor -
Wind.
Str.

-lend bleib' ich hier!
-row I shall die!
animando
Lohengrin. Nie soll dein Reiz ent-schwinden, bleibst du von
Thou ne'er for me shalt sor-row, While thou from
p
p Wind.
mf
Elsa.
Zwei-fel rein! Ach! Dich an mich zu bin-den, wie sollt' ich mäch-tig
doubt art free! What mag-ic can I bor-row To bind thy heart to
Vl.
f
p
cresc.
sein? Voll Zau-ber ist dein We-sen,
me? A spell is cast a-round thee,
f
p
p
durch Wun-der kamst du her:
By mag-ic thou art here;
p
wie sollt' ich da ge-ne-sen?
What ties so-e'er have bound thee,
ff
p

wo fänd' ich dein' Ge-
Thou by a spell canst
cresc.
f più f ff
Recit. (She suddenly starts, violently agitated, and pauses, listening.)
Lohengrin.
währ? Hör-test du nichts? ver-nahmest du kein Kommen? El- sa!
tear! Hark, there are sounds! oh bend thy ear and lis-ten! El- sa!
ff p Vl.
più p
f
Elsa. (gazing vacantly before her.)
poco più lento.
Ach nein! lento. Doch dort, der Schwan, der Schwan! Dort kommt er auf der
A-las! 'Tis there, the swan, the swan! As when I first be-
pp
Fl.& Ob.
Vl.
animandosi.
Lohengrin.
Was-ser-fluth geschwommen, du ru-fest ihm, er zieht her-bei den Kahn! El-sa, halt'
held his pin-ions glis-ten, For thee he comes! ah, must thou now be gone! El-sa, oh
Vivo.
ein! Be-ruh'-ge dei-nen Wahn!
hush! what fan-cies vain are these?
cresc.
Vivo.

Elsa.
Nichts kann mir Ru-he ge-ben, dem Wahn mich nicht ent-
No, thou shalt not compel me To trust, by words of
reisst, als gelt' es auch mein Le-ben! zu
blame, No, not un-less thou tell me Thy
wis-sen, wer du sei'st! Un-se-lig hol-der
country and thy name! What fa-tal spell is
Lohengrin.
El-sa, was willst du wa-gen?
El-sa, oh I con-jure thee?
Mann, hör'! was ich dich muss fra-gen! Den Na-men sag' mir an! Wo-
thine? In vain would'st thou as-sure me: De-clare thy race and name! De-
Halt' ein!
For-bear!
Wind.
Str.
Vl.
Wind.
dim.
Ob.
Tnr., 'Cello, Bssn., & Hns.

(Elsa perceives
her die Fahrt? Wie dei-ne Art?
clare thy name! Where is thy home?
Weh' dir!
Woe's me?
Weh' uns! Was
El-sa! Oh
cresc. più f
ff
Frederick and his four associates, who break in with drawn swords through a door at the back.)
Elsa. (after a shriek)
tha-test du?
mis-er-y!
Ret-te dich!
Save thy-self!
Str.
fp
cresc.
Tpts., Trombs. & Tb.
Dein Schwert, dein Schwert!
Thy sword! thy sword!
(She hastily reaches him his sword, which was by the side of the couch, so that while she holds the sheath he quickly draws it out, and with one blow strikes Frederick, whose arm is uplifted against him, dead. The four Nobles let fall their swords, and sink on their knees before Lohengrin.)
ff
ff
(Elsa, who has thrown herself on Lohengrin's breast, faints, and slowly sinks to the ground. Long silence.)
(Lohengrin, deeply moved, alone remains standing.)
p Hns.
più p
Lento.
K. Dr.
Lohengrin.
p
Weh! Nun ist all' un-ser Glück
Woe, all our joy now is fled
'Cello.
pp
Trombs.
pp
3

(Lohengrin bends down to Elsa and raises her gently, so that she leans against the couch.)

da-hin!
for aye!

Cl. *'Cello.* *pp* *p Str.*

Ob. *Wind. più p*

Elsa. (opening her eyes, faintly.) *p* *pp*

All - e - wi - ger, er-barm' dich mein!
E - ter - nal One, have mer - cy thou!

pp Ped. *pp* *

(On a sign from Lohengrin, the four Nobles rise.)

Lohengrin.

Tragt den Er-schlag'nen vor des Kö - nigs Ge-richt!
Bear hence the corpse in - to the King's judgment-hall!

p *cresc.* *f* *ff Wind.* *p*

Tnr., 'Cello. & D. Bass. Ped. *

(The four Nobles take up Frederick's corpse and depart with it through the door *R. H.*)

Bell.

(Lohengrin pulls a bell, two Ladies enter *L. H.*)

Moderato mosso.

ff Hns. & Trombs. *diminuendo. più p* *pp 'Cello* *p Str.*

Tb., Bssn. & D. Bass.

Lohengrin. *p*

Sie vor den Kö - nig zu ge - lei - ten, schmückt
In - to the roy - al presence lead her, Ar -

p
El - sa, mei - ne sü - sse Frau! Dort will ich Ant-wort ihr be-
ray'd as fits so fair a bride! There all she asks I will con-
p Wood.
rei - ten, dass sie des Gat - ten Art er - schau'!
cede her, Nor from her knowl-edge aught will hide!
(He departs,
Brass.
più p
pp
ff
K. Dr.
sadly and solemnly. The Ladies lead out Elsa, who is speechless, L. H.)
(The day has slowly begun to dawn, the tapers are extinguished.)
Wind. Str.
pp
p Cello.
(A large curtain closes over the front, hiding the stage entirely from view.)
Ob. & Cl.
ff
Wind.
dim.
Cor. ingl. & B. Cl.
B. Cl.
(On the stage.)
mf
dim.
p
più p
pp
4 Tpts. (as though heard from the courtyard.)
ff
(lunga.)
Trombs.
f
p
Tpts.
ff
(On the stage.)

Third Scene.

In the Orchestra.— *3 Flutes, 3 Oboes, 3 Clarinets in B flat, 3 Bassoons, Horns in E flat, 3 Trumpets in C, 3 Trombones, Tuba, 3 Kettle-drums, Strings.*

On the Stage.— *2 Trumpets in E flat, 2 in F, 2 in D, 2 in E, 4 in C, Side-drums.*

(When the curtain is drawn aside, the scene presents the meadow on the bank of the Scheldt, as in the first Act; a brilliant dawn gradually brightens into full daylight.)

Tpts. in D on the stage (approaching rapidly from R. H.)
fp
(nearer and louder.)
cresc. poco a poco.
(Whilst a second
Count enters after the same manner as the first, the trumpets of a third are heard approaching.)
Tpts. in F (from a distance, coming nearer.)
più f
fp
(nearer and louder.)
cresc. poco a poco.
(A third Count enters in the same fashion with his vassals. Each band gathering round its ban-
ff Wind in Orchestra.
f
mf

ner, the Counts and Nobles salute each other, examine and praise each others arms, etc.)

Tpts. in E on the stage (advancing from the background R.H.)
fp
(nearer and louder.)
cresc. poco a poco
f
(A fourth Count enters with his train R.H., and takes up his stand in the centre at the back. When
Tpts. of the King in C.
ffp

the trumpets of the King are sounded, all group themselves in order and unfurl their banners.)

Tpts. in D. *Tpts. in F.*

Tpts. in E flat. *Tpts. in E.* *molto cresc.* *All the Tpts. on the stage.*

(The King with the Saxon arrière-ban enters *L. H.*)

ff *Tutti Orchestra.* *sempre ff*

8

8

Chorus. All the Men. (striking on their shields as the King reaches the oak.)
ff
Heil, Kö - nig Hein - rich!
Hail, roy - al Hen - ry,
ff
Ped.
Kö - nig Hein - rich
roy - al Hen - ry,
Heil!
hail!
On the stage.
f
Tpts. of the King.
All the Tpts. on the stage.
Side Drums (on the stage)
Tpts. in Orch.
f
dim.

The King.

Habt Dank, ihr Lie-ben von Bra-bant!
Have thanks, good lie-ges of Bra-bant!

p Tpts. Trombs. & Tb. cresc. f

Wie fühl' ich stolz mein Herz ent-brannt, find' ich in je-dem deut-schen
Glo-ry in arms may for-tune grant! Great is my pride, that hearts so

Land so kräf-tig rei-chen Heer-ver-band! Nun soll des
brave Go forth our German land to save! Now, 'gainst the

dim.

Rei-ches Feind sich nah'n, wir wol-len ta-pfer ihn em-
wild Hun-ga-rian foe, All are re-solv'd ______ at morn to

fp p

pfahn, aus seinem ö-den Ost da-her soll er sich nimmer wa-gen mehr!
go. Henceforth his dreary East-ern plain Let him not dare to quit a-gain!
mf
cresc.
fp
p
Für deutsches Land das deut-sche Schwert! So sei des Rei-ches Kraft be-
For Ger-man land draw Ger-man sword! Then ye the realm will sure-ly
cresc.
f
mf
p
ff Wind
f mf
währt!
guard!
Chorus. All the Men.
ff
Für deut-sches Land das
For Ger-man land draw
Str.
p molto cresc.
ff Brass
deut-sche Schwert! So sei des Rei-ches Kraft be-währt!
Ger-man sword! Thus we the land shall sure-ly guard!
Tpts on the stage.
ff
ff Tutti

Hns.
The King.
(The men crowd aside as if in dread; the four nobles bring the body of Frederick on a bier, setting it down in the midst of the circle.)
Wo weilt nun der, den Gott ge - sandt zum Ruhm, zur Grö-sse von Brabant?
Where lingers he, the Heav'n-sent knight, Who ev - 'ry vir-tue doth u - nite?
Str.
Hns.
Tb.
The Men (in three Choruses.)
1st Chorus.
2nd Chorus.
3rd Chorus.
Was bringen die?
What do they bear?
Was thun sie kund?
What would they here?
Die Mannen sind's des Tel-ra-mund!
Of Tel-ra-mund they vas-sals are!
Trombs.
The King.
Wen führt ihr her?
Whom do ye bear?
Was soll ich schau'n? Mich fasst bei eurem An-blick Grau'n!
What shall I hear? Some dire event doth bring you here!
Tnr.

The Four Nobles.
Lento.
So will's der Schützer von Brabant: wer dieser ist, macht er bekannt.
E'en by the Guardian of Brabant, Our liege and lord, we here are sent.
Lento.
Ob. & Cl.
Wood.
(Elsa, with a numerous train of Ladies, enters, and comes forward with slow and faltering steps.)
The Men.
(in two Choruses.)
1st Chorus.
Seht, Elsa naht, die Tugendreiche!
Lo, Elsa comes, that lady peerless!
Fl. & Ob.
Tr.
(The King goes to meet Elsa, and leads her to a seat opposite to the oak.)
2nd Chorus.
Wie ist ihr Antlitz trüb' und bleiche!
Her mien is sad, her eye is tearless!
Tr.
più
Cello.
The King.
Wie muss ich dich so traurig sehn! Will dir so nah' die Trennung gehn?
Why do I see thee mourning thus? Cans't thou not bear thy lord to lose?
Wood.
Str.
dim.

A Portion of the Chorus. (at the back.)
(Elsa tries to look up at him, but cannot.)
(Great stir in the background.)
Vivo.
Macht Platz, macht Platz dem Hel - den von Brabant!
Make way, make way, the Guar - dian of Bra - bant!
Vivo.
Str.
p
sf
cresc.
All the Chorus.
ff
(Lohengrin, fully armed, as in Act I, enters and strides solemnly and gravely to the front.)
Heil!
Hail!
Heil dem Hel-den von Bra - bant, dem Hel-den von Bra - bant! Heil!
Hail, thou Guar-dian of Bra - bant, thou Guar-dian of Bra - bant! Hail!
Tutti. ff
Heil dem Hel-den von Bra - bant! Heil!
Hail, thou Guar-dian of Bra - bant! Hail!

Heil: dei - nem Kom - men, theu - rer Held!
Hail, Heav'n-sent he - ro, wel - come here!
Heil!
Hail!
Heil!
Hail!
Str.
p
Wind.
f
K. Dr.
Die du so treu - lich rief'st in's Feld,
Thy loy - al vas - sals all are near,
p
die har-ren dein in Strei - tes Lust, von
Wait-ing for thee to give the word, And
f Wind.
p
f
Str.
p
dir ge - führt, des Sieg's be - wusst.
fight by thy all con - q'ring sword.
fp
f
sf
più f
Str.

Chorus. All the Men.

ff

Wir har - ren dein in Strei - tes Lust, von
We wait for thee to give the word, To

ff

Wind. *Brass.*

ff

Ped. * Ped. * Ped. *

dir ge - führt, des Sieg's be - wusst.
fight by thy all con - q'ring sword.

ff

Ped.

Lohengrin. **Più moderato.**

Mein Herr und Kö - nig, lass dir mel - den:
My gra - cious sov'reign, bear me blameless,

Str. Tpts. & Trombs.

mf p

*

die ich be - rief, die küh - nen Hel - den, zum Streit sie füh - ren darf ich
Rea - sons have I, that must be name - less, The des - tin'd campaign I sus -

p p f f

Lento.
The King. ff
nicht!
pend!
(All express the utmost consternation.)
Hilf
A-
All the Men.
Hilf
A-
Hilf
What
Lento.
f Fl. & Tr.
Wind.
Lohengrin.
Gott! Welch' har-tes Wort er spricht!
las! What can his words por-tend!
Als Streit-ge-noss bin nicht ich her-ge-
To lead ye forth to bat-tle here I
Hilf Gott!
A- las!
The Ladies.
Gott! Welch' har-tes Wort er spricht!
las! What can his words por-tend?
Gott! Welch' har - tes Wort!
can his words por - tend?
Tpts. & Trombs.
Str.
(He uncovers Frederick's corpse, from which all turn with horror.)
kommen; als Klä-ger sei ich jetzt von euch ver-nommen!
came not; But judge me, for your le-nien-cy I claim not!
cresc.
Trombs.
Str.

(solemnly, standing by the corpse.)
Zum er-sten kla-ge laut ich vor euch
Then first-ly, do ye hold that I am
Wind.
D. Bass, Trombs & Tb.
lento.
Al - len, und frag' um Spruch nach Recht und Fug: da die-ser
guil - ty? Your just de-cree to me is due: He sought my
Str.
Mann zur Nacht mich über-fal-len, sagt, ob ich ihn mit Recht erschlug?
life, de-spite hon-or and feal-ty, Say, did I right when him I slew?
The King and all the Men (all solemnly stretching forth their hands towards the corpse.)
Wie dei-ne Hand ihn schlug auf Er-den, soll dort ihm
E'en as thy sword in earth has laid him, The saints will
Tpts. & Trombs.
Str.
Lohengrin.
Zum an-dern aber sollt ihr
And fur-ther, I declare in
Got-tes Stra - fe wer-den!
sure re-fuse to aid him!
12946

Kla - ge hö - ren, denn al - ler Welt nun klag' ich laut, dass zum Ver-
face of Heav - en, Though bit - ter grief to me it bode: That from her

Wind. Str.

rath an mir sich liess be - thö - ren das Weib, das Gott mir an - ge-
fair al - legiance hath been driv - en, The wife that Heav'n on me be -

Wind.

The King.

Adagio.

traut! El - sa! Wie konntest du dich so ver - geh'n?
stow'd! El - sa! Oh El - sa, say, what hast thou done?

Chorus of Ladies. (looking reproachfully towards Elsa.)

SOPRANO & ALTO.

We - he dir! El - sa!
Woe is thine! El - sa!

Chorus of Men. (with grief and consternation.)

TENOR.

El - sa! Wie moch - te das ge - scheh'n? Wie konntest so du dich ver - geh'n?
El - sa! say, oh what hast thou done? Sentence so stern how hast thou won?

BASS.

Adagio. Str. dim.

Lohengrin (sternly.)

lento.

Ihr hör - tet Al - le, wie sie mir versprochen, dass nie sie woll' er - fra - gen, wer ich
Ye all have heard her give her word in to - ken, That she my name and country ne'er would

dim.

bin? Nun hat sie ih-ren theuren Schwur ge-brochen, treu-lo-sem
ask; That promise her im-pa-tient heart hath broken, Vain-ly I
p
cresc.
Wind.
fp
Str.
f
dim. p
fp
Ped.
(all express the utmost agitation.)
Rath gab sie ihr Herz da-hin! Zu
hop'd she would ful-fil her task! Her
ff
loh-nen ih-res Zweifels wil-dem Fra-gen, sei nun die Antwort län-ger nicht ge-
questions, her in-ju-rious doubts constrain me, What she de-sires to know, here to de-
Brass.
ffp
dim.
spart; des Fein-des Drängen durft' ich sie ver-sagen; nun muss ich
clare; The foe I scorn'd who ventur'd to arraign me, But she may
p Tpts. & Trombs.
Con moto moderato.
(his face gradually becomes transfigured.)
kün-den, wie mein Nam' und Art! Jetzt merket wohl, ob ich den Tag muss
claim to know the name I bear! Now mark me well, I will no more with-
più p
pp
K. Dr.

scheu - en! Vor al - ler Welt, vor Kö - nig und vor Reich ent - hül - le mein Ge -
hold it! Nor have I cause to shrink from a - ny test; When I my name and

Trombs.& Tb. sustain

pp

heim - niss ich in Treu - en.
lin - eage have un - fold - ed, *poco a poco rall.*

(Rising to his utmost height.)

So
Ye'll

pp

hört, ob ich an A - del euch nicht
know that I am no - ble as the

sempre pp

Lento.

The King.

pp

gleich! Wass muss ich nun er - fah - ren? O, könnt' er die
best! What is this fa - tal se - cret? Oh would that this

Chorus. TENOR.

pp

Welch' Un - er - hör - tes muss ich nun er - fah - ren? O, könnt' er die erzwung' - ne
What is this se - cret he so well hath guarded? Oh, that this fa - tal hour, this

BASS I.

pp

Welch' Un - er - hör - tes muss ich nun er - fah - ren? O, könnt' er die erzwung' - ne
What is this se - cret he so well hath guarded? Oh, that this fa - tal hour, this

BASS II.

pp

Lento.

O, könnt' er die Kun -
Oh, had but this hour

Cl.

Str.

pp

Kun-de sich er-spa - ren!
hour had been re-tard - ed!

Kun-de sich er-spa - ren!
hour had been re-tard - ed!

Kun-de sich er-spa - ren!
hour had been re-tard - ed!

de er-spa - ren!
been re-tard - ed!

3 Fl. & Ob.

pp Brass sustain. Vl. con Sord.

Ped. *

Lohengrin.

Lento.

In fer-nem Land, un-nah-bar eu-ren Schritten,
In dis-tant land, by ways re-mote and hid-den,

Vl.

pp *pp*

Ped. * Ped.

liegt ei-ne Burg, die Mon-sal-vat genannt; ein lich-ter Tem-pel ste-het
There stands a Burg that men call Mon-sal-vat; It holds a shrine to the pro-

Vl.

pp Fl. & Ob. sustain.

* Ped.

dort in-mit-ten, so kost-bar, als auf Er-den nichts be-kannt; drin ein Ge-
fane for-bid-den, More pre-cious there is naught on earth than that; And, thron'd in

p Vl. & Tnr. only

* Ped. *

fäss von wun-der-thät-gem Se-gen wird dort als höch-stes Hei-ligthum bewacht: es
light, it holds a cup im-mor-tal, That who-so sees, from earth-ly sin is cleansd; Twas
ward, dass sein der Men-schen rein-ste pfle-gen, her-ab von ei-ner En-gel-
borne by an-gels thro' the heav'n-ly por-tal, Its com-ing hath a ho-ly
schaar-ge-bracht; all-jähr-lich naht vom Him-mel ei-ne Tau-be, um
reign commenc'd. Once ev-'ry year, a dove from Heav'n descend-eth, To
neu zu stärken sei-ne Wun-der-kraft: es heisst der Gral, und se-lig rein-ster
strengthen it a-new for works of grace; 'Tis call'd the Grail, the pow'r of Heav'n at-
Glau-be ertheilt durch ihn sich sei-ner Rit-ter-schaft. Wer nun dem
tend-eth The faith-ful knights who guard that sa-cred place. He whom the
p
pp
Vl.
f
cresc.
Tur., 'Cello, Trombs. & Tb.

Gral zu dienen ist er - ko - ren, den rü - stet er mit ü - ber-ir-discher
Grail to be its serv-ant choos-es, Is arm'd henceforth with high, in-vin-ci-ble
mf
p
più p
Ped.
Macht; an dem ist je - des Bö - sen Trug ver-lo - ren, wenn
might; All e - vil craft its pow'r be-fore him los-es, the
ihn er er-sieht, weicht dem des To - des Nacht. Selbst wer von ihm in fer-ne
spir-its of dark-ness, where he dwells, take flight. Nor will he lose the aw-ful
p
Land' entsendet, zum Strei-ter für der Tugend Recht er-nannt, dem wird nicht sei-ne
charm it lendeth, Al-though he should be call'd to dis-tant lands, When the high cause of
p
heil-ge Kraft ent-wendet, bleibt als sein Rit-ter dort er un-er-kannt: so
vir-tue he de-fendeth, While he's un-known, its spell he still com-mands; By
Fl.
f
p
pp Tpts. & Trombs.
p
più p
Ped.
Ped.
Ped.

heh-rer Art doch ist des Gra-les Se-gen, ent-hüllt, muss er des Lai-en Au-ge
per-ils dread the ho-ly Grail is gird-ed, No eye rash or pro-fane its light may
Vl.
p
fliehn: des Rit-ters drum sollt Zweifel ihr nicht he-gen, erkennt ihr ihn, dann muss er
see; Its champion knight from doubtings shall be warded, If known to man, he must de-
dim.
ff
von euch ziehn. Nun hört, wie ich ver-bot'ner Fra-ge
part and flee. Now mark, craft or dis-guise my soul dis-
Wind.
Str.
Tpt.
cresc.
loh-ne! Vom Gral ward ich zu euch da-her ge-sandt; mein Va-ter Par-zi-val
dain-eth, The Grail sent me to right yon la-dy's fame; My fa-ther, Per-ci-val,
ff Wind.
f
trägt sei-ne Kro-ne, sein Rit-ter ich bin Lo-hengrin ge-nannt.
glo-riously reigneth, His knight am I, and Lo-hengrin my name.
Trombs & Tpts.
ff Tutti.

The King.
Adagio.
p
Hör' ich so sei - ne
While I hear him the
The Men.
TENOR I.
pp
Hör' ich so sei - ne höch - ste Art be -
While I hear him the won - drous tale re -
TENOR II.
p
Hör' ich so ihn
While I hear him,
BASS I.
p
Hör' ich so sei - ne
While I hear him the
BASS II.
p
Hör' ich so sei - ne
While the tale he re -
ritard.
dim.
p
pp Adagio.
8
höch - ste Art be - wäh - ren. ent - brennt mein Aug' in
won - drous tale re - veal - ing, The ho - ly tears a -
(with great emotion.)
SOPRANO.
pp
Hör' ich so sei - ne höch - ste Art be - wäh - ren, ent - brennt mein Aug' in
While I hear him the won - drous tale re - veal - ing, The ho - ly tears a -
ALTO.
p
Hör' ich die Kun - de, ent - brennt mein
Ah, while I hear him, the tears a -
wäh - ren,
veal - ing,
p
ent -
the
sei - ne Art be - wäh - ren, ent - brennt mein Au -
ho - ly tears a - down my cheek are steal -
höch - ste Art be - wäh - ren, ent - brennt mir das
won - drous tale re - veal - ing, The tears, the
Art, ent - brennt mein Aug' in
veals, the ho - ly tears a -

Elsa (crushed.)
heil' - gen Won - ne - zäh - ren!
down my cheek are steal - ing!
Mir schwankt der
'Tis dark a-
heil'-gen Won-ne-zäh-ren!
down my cheek are steal-ing!
Aug' in Won - ne - zäh - ren!
down my cheek are steal - ing!
pp
brennt mein Aug' in heil'-gen Won - ne - zäh - ren!
ho - ly tears a-down my cheek are steal - ing!
più p
ge in Won - ne - zäh - ren!
ing, a - down are steal - ing!
più p
Aug' in heil' - gen Won - ne - zäh - ren!
tears a - down my cheek are steal - ing!
più p
heil' - gen Won - ne - zäh - ren!
down my cheek are steal - ing!
più p
pp
K. Dr.
'Cello.
accel.
Bo - den! Wel-che Nacht! O Luft, Luft der Unglück - sel' - gen!
round me! Give me air! Oh help, help! oh me most wretch-ed!
Tnr.
cresc.
Vlns.
All the Str.
p molto cresc.
(As she is falling, Lohengrin catches her in his arms.)
Lohengrin.
Vivo.
più lento.
Allegro, a tempo.
O, El-sa! Was hast du mir an-ge-than?
Oh El-sa! Why hast thou our joy un-done?
Wind.
Str.
f
p
f
p
Ped.
*
Ped.
*

Als mei-ne Au-gen dich zu-erst — er-sah'n, zu dir fühlt' —
Since on my path thy radiant glanc-es shone, I felt thou —
Ped.
— ich in Lie- - be mich entbrannt, und schnell hatt' ich ein neues
— wert the soul — of all de-light, Thy love brought to my life a
riten.
Wind.
f dim.
Ped.
a tempo.
Glück er-kannt; die heh-re Macht, die Wunder meiner Art, die
glo-ry bright. The pow'r I own, my heav'n-appointed fate, The
Str.
riten.
ritard.
Kraft, die mein Ge-heim-niss mir bewahrt, wollt' — ich dem Dienst des reinsten
trust, no pow'r of earth can ab-ro-gate, I — thought that these must o'er thy
lento.
Wind.
p riten.
più p
pp
Ped.
Vivo.
Herzens weih'n: — was ris-sest du nun mein Geheimniss ein? Jetzt — muss ich
doubts pre-vail: Why would thy heart distrustful rend the veil? Ah, — me, a-
Str.
f Wind.
Vivo. p
cresc. fp
Ped.

Vivo.
ach! von dir ge - schie - den sein!
las! Now I must say — fare - well!
Elsa (starting in wild despair.)
Mein Gat - te! Nein! ich
My con - sort! No! we
The King.
Weh'! Weh'!
Woe! woe!
Chorus of Ladies.
SOPRANO and ALTO.
Weh'! Weh'!
Woe! woe!
Chorus of Men.
TENOR.
Weh'! Weh'! Weh'!
Woe! woe! woe!
BASS.
Vivo.
Tutti.
più f
lass' dich nicht von hin - nen! Als Zeu - ge meiner Bu - sse
can - not thus be part - ed! Re - morse and woe con - sume me,
blei - be hier, als Zeu - ge mei - ner Bu - sse
stay, oh stay! re - morse and woe consume me,

blei - be hier!
stay, oh stay!
Lohengrin.
Ich muss, ich muss! mein süsses
A - las, I must, my sweet-est
Wind.
Weib!
wife!
Nicht darfst du mei-ner bit-tern Reu' ent-
Ah no, thou wilt not leave me brok - en-
Chorus. SOPRANO and ALTO.
Weh'!
Woe!
Weh', nun
Ah, must
TENOR.
Weh'!
Woe!
BASS.
Str.
rin - nen; dass du mich stra - fest,
heart - ed; See my re-pent - ance,
muss er von
thou for ev -

lie - ge ich vor dir, dass du mich
at thy feet I pray, see my re -
dir
er
zieh'n!
go?
fp
p
stra - fest, lie-ge ich vor dir!
pent - ance, at thy feet I pray!
Lohengrin.
Ich muss, ich
A - las! I
Wind.
Str.
f
>p
fp
cresc.
Elsa.
muss, mein sü - sses Weib!
must, my sweet - est wife!
The King.
SOPRANO & ALTO.
TENOR.
f
Weh'! We - he!
Woe! Woe! must
BASS.
f
Wind.
Str.
f
dim.
fp
cresc.

Bist du so gött - lich, als ich dich er-kannt, sei Got-tes
If thou'rt from Heav - en, as I do be-lieve, Mer - cy di-
Weh'! ach, musst du von uns zieh'n, du heh -
Woe! must thou for ev-er go? Ah, must
Weh'!
Woe!
Weh', du heh -
woe! Ah, must
Musst du von uns zieh'n, du heh - rer, gott - ge-sand-ter Mann!
thou for ev - er go! ah, must we lose thee, Heav'n-sent knight?
Wind.
Str.
dim.
dimin.

Gna-de nicht aus dir — ver-bannt!
vine within thy heart must live!
Schon zürnt der Gral.
The Grail doth call,
p
rer, gott - ge - sand - ter Mann!
we lose thee, Heav'n - sent knight?
- rer, gott-ge - sand - ter Mann!
— we lose thee, Heav'n - sent knight?
f
Soll
No
p
We - he!
Ah me!
f
fp
p
Ped.
Büsst sie in
Grief and re -
dass ich ihm fer - - ne
far from all earth - - ly
f
Soll uns des
No hope of
più f
uns des Him - mels Se - gen
hope of bliss re - mains be -
più f
cresc.

Jam - - mer ih - re schwe-re Schuld: nicht flieh' die
morse my tor - tur'd spir - it tear, Thy pres-ence
bleib'!
strife!
dim.
Him - mels Se - gen flieh'n, wo fän - den
bliss re - mains be - low when thou from
f
dim.
fän
us
Weh'!
Woe!
Ach, wo fän -
when from us
ff
dim.
p
flieh'n, wo fän-den dein' wir Trö - stung dann?
low, when thou from us hast tak - en flight!
Wind.
Str.
dimin.
Aermste dei-ner Nä - he Huld! Ver - stoss' mich
dear thou wilt in pit - y spare! Oh spurn me
Ich muss! Ich muss! Nur
A - las! I must! One
dein' wir Trö - stung dann? Soll
us hast tak - en flight! No
den
thou'st
- den Trost wir dann? Weh'
thou'st tak - en flight! Ah
fp
O bleib'!
Oh stay!
fp

nicht! Ver - stoss' mich nicht, wie gross auch mein Ver-
not! Oh spurn me not, though great was my trans-
ei - ne Stra - fe giebt's für dein Ver-
sole a - tonement Heav'n for thee de -
uns des Him - mels Se -
hope of bliss re - mains
uns! Weh' uns! Wo
me! Ah me! no
O bleib'! O bleib'!
Oh stay, oh stay!
bre - chen; Ver - lass,
gres - sion! Have mer -
geh'n! Ach! mich, wie
crees! I bear it
- gen flieh'n, wo fän - den
be - low when thou from
fän - den dein' wir
hope of bliss re -
Wo fän - den dein' wir
No hope of bliss re -
molto cresc.
Ped.
Ped.

ach, ver - lass mich Aermste nicht! Ver-lass mich nicht, ver-lass
cy, oh leave me not to die! In pit-y turn, in pit-
dich trifft ih-re her - be Pein! Mich, wie dich
too, thou'rt not more lone than I! Ah, my love,
Trost wir dann?
us art gone!
Trö - stung dann?
mains be - low!
Trö - stung dann?
mains be - low!
dim.
mich nicht! Ach! ver-lass, ver-lass
y turn! leave me not to die,
trifft ih - re her - be Pein!
thou'rt not more lone than I!
O blei - be! Wo
Oh tar - ry! No
Wo
No
Wo
No
cresc. molto.

die Ar- - - - - me
to die a-
Ge-
The
fän- - den Trö- - - - stung
bliss re- mains be-
fän- den Trö- - - stung
bliss re- mains be-
fän- - den Trö- - - stung
bliss re- mains be-
più f
nicht!
lone!
trennt, ge- schie- den sol- len wir uns
fate that parts us, thus we shall ap-
wir?
low!
wir?
low!
wir?
low!
Vl.
ff
Wind.

seh'n:
pease,
dies
Here
muss die
dwell in
Stra-
sor-
-fe,
-row,
dies
till
die
we
Süh-
meet
-ne
on
sein!
high!
(Elsa falls back with a cry.)
The King.
O bleib'!
Oh stay!
All the Men. (impetuously crowding around Lohengrin.)
O
Oh
bleib'!
stay!
O
Oh
Vl. & Tbr.
O bleib', und zieh' uns nicht von
Oh stay! with-draw thy stern a-
bleib', und zieh' uns nicht von dan-nen! Des Füh-rers har-ren dei-ne
stay! with-draw thy stern a-void-ance! Thy trust-y war-riors ask thy
bleib', zieh' uns nicht von dan-nen!
can- -cel thy stern a-void-ance!
Fl. & Cl.

dan - nen! Des Füh - rers har-ren dei-ne Man-nen!
void - ance! Thy trust - y war-riors ask thy guid-ance!
Man-nen, des Füh-rers har-ren dei-ne Man - nen! O bleib', und zieh' uns
guid-ance, thy trust-y warriors ask thy guid - ance, oh stay, with-draw thy
Des Füh - rers har-ren dei-ne Man - nen! O bleib', und zieh' uns
Thy trust - y warriors ask thy guid - ance, oh stay, with-draw thy
ff
O bleib'! Zieh' uns nicht von dannen! Des Führers har - ren dei-ne Man-
Oh stay, can-cel thy a - voidance! Thy trusty war - riors seek thy guid-
nicht von dan - nen! Des Füh-rers, des Führers har-ren dei-ne Man -
stern a - void - ance! Thy war-riors, thy trusty warriors seek thy guid -
nicht von dan - nen! Des Füh-rers, ja, har-ren dei - ne Man -
stern a - void - ance! Thy war-riors, thy warriors seek thy guid -
Lohengrin.
Animato e vivo.
nen! O Kö - nig, hör'! Ich darf dich nicht ge-lei-ten! Des Gra-les Rit-ter,—
ance! Give heed, oh King! In fight I may not lead them! The Grail's sworn champion,
nen!
ance!
nen!
ance!
f
ff
Wind.
ff
Str.
fp
colla parte.

habt ihr ihn er-kannt,—wollt' er in Un-ge-hor-sam mit euch strei-ten,—
if to mor-tals known, Must bide its laws, and in o-bedience heed them;
ihm wä-re al-le Man-nes-kraft ent-wandt!—
Or ev-'ry pow'r of manhood he'd dis-own!
Doch, grosser
Mark, roy-al
ffp
p
ff
p
Kö-nig! lass mich dir weis-sagen:—
Hen-ry, what my heart pre-sages!
Dir Reinem ist ein gro-sser Sieg ver-
Thou shalt a glo-rious war with vic-t'ry
Ob. Cl. & Hns.
Str.
p
più moderato.
lieh'n!
crown!
Nach Deutschland sol-len noch in fernsten Tagen, des
In Ger-man land thro' dis-tant fu-ture ages, No
Tpts.
ff
p
(general excitement.)
Ostens Hor-den siegreich nim-mer zieh'n!
Eastern horde shall ev-er win re-nown!
cresc.
f
ff Allegro.

Some of the Men (at the back.)
The Men in the Foreground (turning towards the back.)
TENOR I.II.
BASS I.II.
Der Schwan! der Schwan! Der Schwan! Seht dort ihn wie-der nah'n!
The swan! the swan! The swan! Yon stream he float-eth down!
Der Schwan!
The swan!
p Str.
Wind sustain.
The Ladies (not far from the front, round Elsa.)
SOPRANO.
ALTO.
Der Schwan! Weh', er naht!
The swan! Ah, he comes!
Der Schwan! Weh', er naht!
The swan! Ah, he comes!
Er naht, der Schwan!
He comes, the swan!
poco cresc.
(Elsa, waking from her stupor, rises, leaning on her seat, and looks towards the bank.)
Elsa.
Entsetzlich
Oh horror!
(Here the swan passes round the front bend of the stream; he draws the empty skiff.)
Wind.
fp
dimin.
ff
p
12946

(She remains for a long time like one petrified in the same position.)
Lohengrin (deeply moved.)
Ha! der Schwan!
Ah! the swan!
Schon sendet nach dem Säumigen der Gral!
Too long I stay, I must obey the Grail!
Tpts.& Trombs.
cresc.
ff
dim.
p
pp
Str.
(While all stand with strained attention, Lohengrin advances to the bank and bends over the swan.)
Andante moderato.
Mein lie - ber
My trust - y
Vlns.only.
Schwan! Ach, die - se letz - te, traur'ge Fahrt, wie gern hätt' ich sie dir_ erspart!
swan! Oh that this summons ne'er had been! Oh that this day I ne'er had seen!
In ei - nem Jahr, wenn dei - ne Zeit im Dienst zu En - de soll - te gehn,
I thought the year soon would be o'er, When thy pro - bation would have pass'd;
mf
dann, durch des Gra - les Macht be - freit, wollt' ich dich an - ders wie - der seh'n!
Then, by the Grail's transcendent_ pow'r, In thy true shape we'd meet at last!

(He returns to the front towards Elsa, with an outburst of anguish.)
Oh
Vivo.
p molto cresc.
ff Tutti.
El-sa! Nur ein Jahr an dei-ner Sei-te hätt' ich als
El-sa, think what joys thy doubts have end-ed! Couldst thou not
Str.
ff
fp
ritard.
più moderato.
Zeu-ge dei-nes Glücks er-sehnt! Dann kehr-te, se-lig in des
trust in me for one short year? Then thy dear brother, whom the
Wind.
p
fp
Andante moderato.
(all express extreme
Gral's Ge-lei-te, dein Bru-der wieder, den du todt ge-wähnt.
Grail de-fend-ed, In life and honor thou hadst wel-com'd here.
Str.
fp
cresc.
p
astonishment.)
8
f